# Standard Songs
## of
# EVANGELISM

*Compiled from
Editorial Suggestions submitted by
136 Active Evangelists and
Evangelistic Music Directors*

PUBLISHED IN ROUND NOTES ONLY

TABERNACLE PUBLISHING CO.
350 North Waller Avenue
CHICAGO · · ILLINOIS

HOPE PUBLISHING CO.
5707 West Lake Street
CHICAGO · · ILLINOIS

Printed in U. S. A.
1942

# Preface

THE gospel songs and hymns contained in this book have become standard by reason of their long association with all religious meetings of an evangelistic character.

Another distinguishing feature is the omission of all songs of an experimental nature.

We wish to acknowledge our obligation, and also express our cordial appreciation, to the one hundred and thirty-six active evangelists and evangelistic music directors from whose editorial suggestions this book has been compiled.

THE PUBLISHERS.

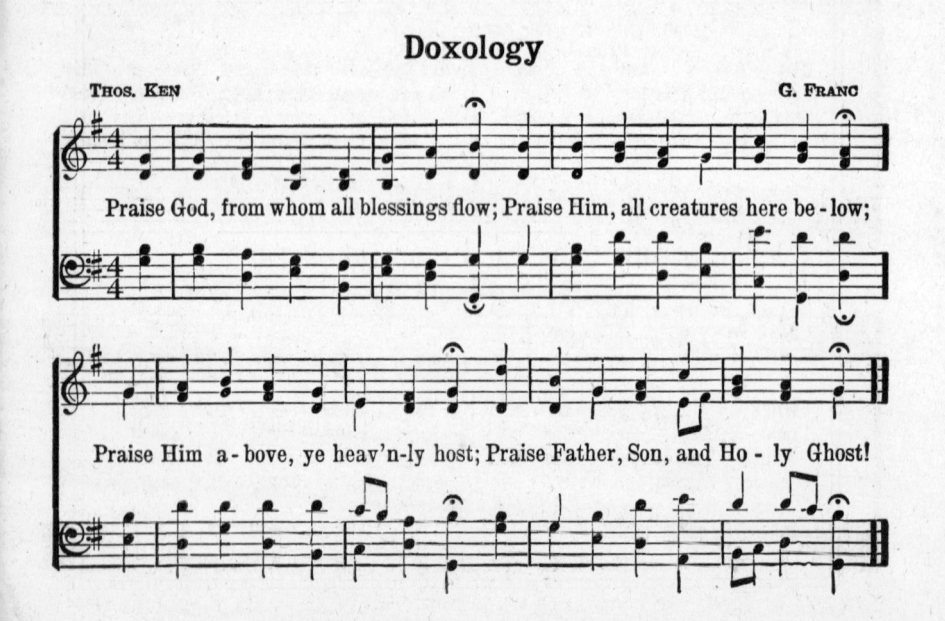

## Doxology

THOS. KEN          G. FRANC

Praise God, from whom all blessings flow; Praise Him, all creatures here be-low;

Praise Him a-bove, ye heav'n-ly host; Praise Father, Son, and Ho-ly Ghost!

# STANDARD SONGS
## OF
# EVANGELISM

## Have Thine Own Way, Lord

A. A. P.

GEO. C. STEBBINS

*Slowly*

1. Have Thine own way, Lord! Have Thine own way!.. Thou art the Pot-ter; I am the clay... Mould me and make me Aft-er Thy will,.... While I am wait-ing, Yield-ed and still...
2. Have Thine own way, Lord! Have Thine own way!.. Search me and try me, Mas-ter, to-day!... Whit-er than snow, Lord, Wash me just now,.... As in Thy pres-ence Hum-bly I bow...
3. Have Thine own way, Lord! Have Thine own way!.. Wound-ed and wea-ry, Help me, I pray!. Pow-er—all pow-er—Sure-ly is Thine! Touch me and heal me, Sav-ior di-vine!..
4. Have Thine own way, Lord! Have Thine own way!.. Hold o'er my be-ing Ab-so-lute sway!. Fill with Thy Spir-it Till all shall see.... Christ on-ly, al-ways, Liv-ing in me!....

Copyright, 1907, by Geo. C. Stebbins       Hope Publishing Company, owner

# 2  The Old Rugged Cross

Rev. G. B.  
Rev. Geo. Bennard

1. On a hill far a-way stood an old rug-ged cross, The em-blem of suf-f'ring and shame; And I love that old cross where the dear-est and best For a world of lost sin-ners was slain.
2. Oh, that old rug-ged cross so de-spised by the world, Has a wondrous at-trac-tion for me; For the dear Lamb of God left His glo-ry a-bove, To bear it to dark Cal-va-ry.
3. In the old rug-ged cross, stained with blood so di-vine, A won-drous beau-ty I see; For 'twas on that old cross Je-sus suf-fered and died, To par-don and sanc-ti-fy me.
4. To the old rug-ged cross I will ev-er be true, Its shame and re-proach gladly bear; Then He'll call me some day to my home far a-way, Where His glo-ry for-ev-er I'll share.

CHORUS

So I'll cher-ish the old rug-ged cross, the old rug-ged cross,.... Till my tro-phies at last I lay down; I will cling to the old rugged cross, the old rug-ged cross,..... And ex-change it some day for a crown.

Copyright, 1913, by Geo. Bennard. Homer A. Rodeheaver, owner

# 3. Love Lifted Me

JAMES ROWE  
HOWARD E. SMITH

1. I was sinking deep in sin, Far from the peaceful shore, Very deeply stained within, Sinking to rise no more; But the Master of the sea Heard my despairing cry, From the waters lifted me, Now safe am I.
2. All my heart to Him I give, Ever to Him I'll cling, In His blessed presence live, Ever His praises sing. Love so mighty and so true Merits my soul's best songs; Faithful, loving service, too, To Him belongs.
3. Souls in danger, look above, Jesus completely saves; He will lift you by His love Out of the angry waves. He's the Master of the sea, Billows His will obey; He your Savior wants to be—Be saved today.

**CHORUS**

Love lifted me!.... (even me!) Love lifted me!.... (even me!) When nothing else could help, Love lifted me. Love lifted me.

Copyright, 1912, by Charlie D. Tillman. Robert H. Coleman, owner

# 4. I Will Sing the Wondrous Story

F. H. ROWLEY  
PETER P. BILHORN

1. I will sing the wondrous story Of the Christ who died for me,
2. I was lost, but Jesus found me, Found the sheep that went astray,
3. I was bruised, but Jesus healed me; Faint was I from many a fall;
4. Days of darkness still come o'er me, Sorrow's paths I often tread,
5. He will keep me till the river Rolls its waters at my feet;

How He left His home in glory For the cross of Calvary.
Threw His loving arms around me, Drew me back into His way.
Sight was gone, and fears possessed me, But He freed me from them all.
But the Savior still is with me; By His hand I'm safely led.
Then He'll bear me safely over, Where the loved ones I shall meet.

**CHORUS**

Yes, I'll sing the wondrous story Of the Christ who died for me,
Sing it with the saints in glory, Gathered by the crystal sea.

Words and Music Copyrighted 1887 by Ira D. Sankey, Renewal 1914 by P. P. Bilhorn

# He Keeps Me Singing

L. B. B.         L. B. BRIDGERS

1. There's within my heart a mel-o-dy Je-sus whis-pers sweet and low,
2. All my life was wrecked by sin and strife, Dis-cord filled my heart with pain,
3. Feast-ing on the rich-es of His grace, Resting 'neath His shelt'ring wing,
4. Tho' sometimes He leads thro' waters deep, Tri-als fall a-cross the way,
5. Soon He's com-ing back to wel-come me Far be-yond the star-ry sky;

Fear not, I am with thee, peace, be still, In all of life's ebb and flow.
Je-sus swept across the broken strings, Stirred the slumb'ring chords again.
Al-ways look-ing on His smil-ing face, That is why I shout and sing.
Tho' sometimes the path seems rough and steep, See His footprints all the way.
I shall wing my flight to worlds un-known, I shall reign with Him on high.

**CHORUS.**

Je-sus, Je-sus, Je-sus,— Sweet-est name I know,
Fills my ev-'ry long-ing, Keeps me sing-ing as I go. A-MEN.

Copyright, 1910, by L. B. Bridgers. Robert H. Coleman, owner

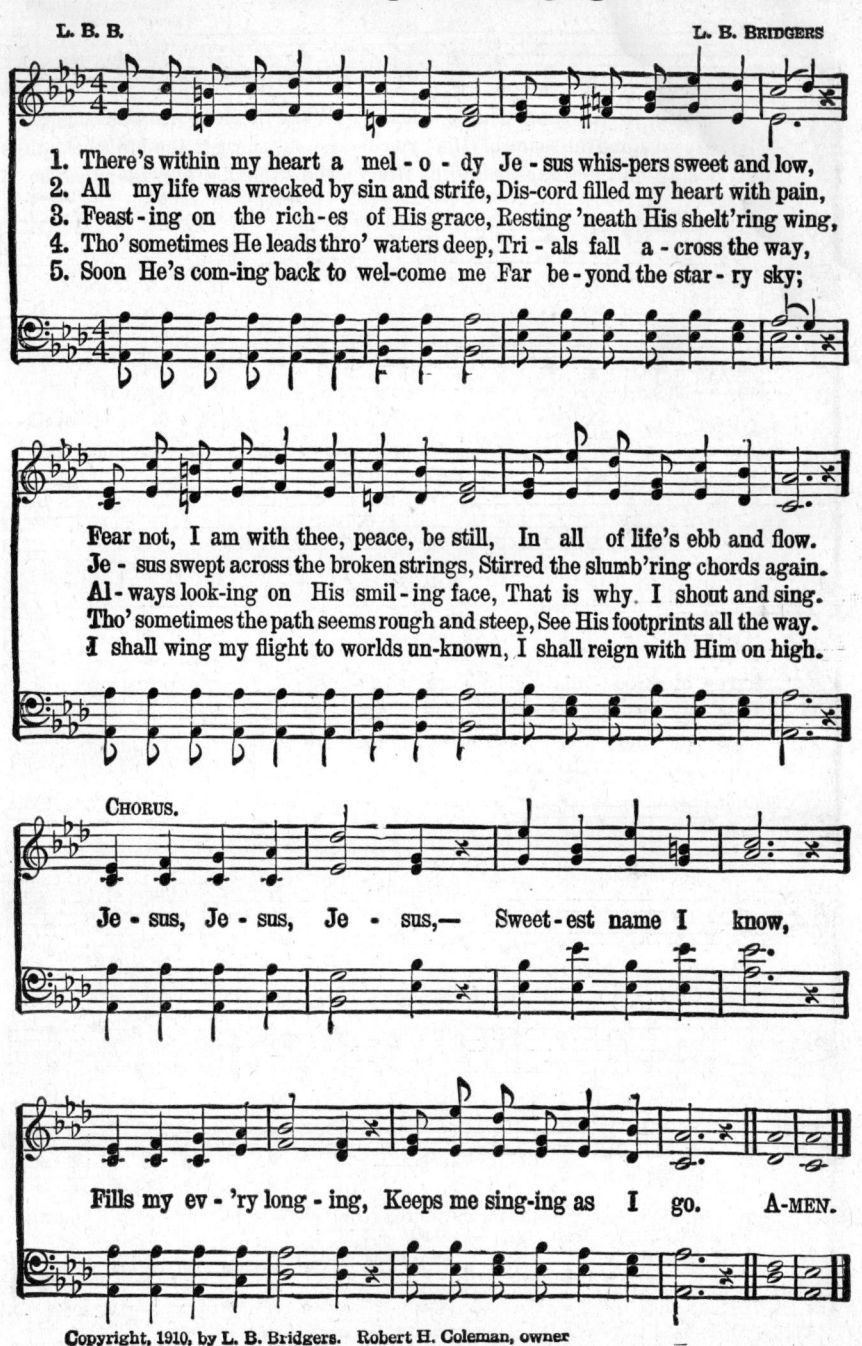

# 6  In The Garden

C. A. M.  
C. Austin Miles

1. I come to the gar-den a-lone, While the dew is still on the ros-es, And the voice I hear, Fall-ing on my ear, The Son of God dis-clos-es.
2. He speaks, and the sound of His voice Is so sweet the birds hush their sing-ing, And the mel-o-dy That He gave to me, With-in my heart is ring-ing.
3. I'd stay in the gar-den with Him Tho' the night a-round me be fall-ing, But He bids me go; Thro' the voice of woe His voice to me is call-ing.

**Chorus**

And He walks with me, and He talks with me, And He tells me I am His own; And the joy we share as we tar-ry there, None oth-er has ev-er known.

Copyright, 1912, by Hall-Mack Co. International Copyright secured

# 7  Christ Arose

ROBERT LOWRY  
ROBERT LOWRY

1. Low in the grave He lay— Je-sus my Sav-ior! Wait-ing the com-ing day—
2. Vain-ly they watch His bed— Je-sus my Sav-ior! Vain-ly they seal the dead—
3. Death cannot keep his prey— Je-sus my Sav-ior! He tore the bars a-way—

REFRAIN *Faster*

Je-sus my Lord! Up from the grave He a-rose, (He a-rose,) With a might-y tri-umph o'er His foes; (He a-rose!) He a-rose a Vic-tor from the dark do-main, And He lives for-ev-er with His saints to reign. He a-rose! He a-rose! Hal-le-lu-jah! Christ a-rose!
He a-rose! He a-rose!

Copyright, 1916, by Mary Runyon Lowry. Renewal. Used by permission

# 8. Since Jesus Came Into My Heart

R. H. McDaniel
Chas. H. Gabriel

1. What a won-der-ful change in my life has been wrought Since Je-sus came
2. I have ceased from my wand'ring and go-ing a-stray, Since Je-sus came
3. I'm pos-sessed of a hope that is stead-fast and sure, Since Je-sus came
4. There's a light in the val-ley of death now for me, Since Je-sus came
5. I shall go there to dwell in that Cit-y, I know, Since Je-sus came

in-to my heart! I have light in my soul for which long I had sought,
in-to my heart! And my sins, which were man-y, are all washed a-way,
in-to my heart! And no dark clouds of doubt now my path-way ob-scure,
in-to my heart! And the gates of the Cit-y be-yond I can see,
in-to my heart! And I'm hap-py, so hap-py, as on-ward I go,

## Chorus

Since Je-sus came in-to my heart! Since Je-sus came in-to my
Since Je-sus came in, came

heart, Since Je-sus came in-to my heart, Floods of joy o'er my
in-to my heart, Since Je-sus came in, came in-to my heart,

soul like the sea bil-lows roll, Since Je-sus came in-to my heart.

Copyright, 1914, by Chas. H. Gabriel. Homer A. Rodeheaver, owner.

# 9. In My Heart There Rings a Melody

E. M. R.  
Elton M. Roth

1. I have a song that Jesus gave me, It was sent from heav'n above; There never was a sweeter melody, 'Tis a melody of love.
2. I love the Christ who died on Cal-v'ry, For He washed my sins away; He put within my heart a melody, And I know it's there to stay.
3. 'Twill be my endless theme in glory, With the angels I will sing; 'Twill be a song with glorious harmony, When the courts of heaven ring.

**Chorus**

In my heart there rings a melody, There rings a melody with heaven's harmony; In my heart there rings a melody; There rings a melody of love.

Copyright. 1923, by Elton M. Roth. E. O. Excell, Jr., owner

# 10 Saved, Saved!

J. P. S.                                                             J. P. SCHOLFIELD

1. I've found a friend who is all to me,.... His love is ev-er true;...... I love to tell how He lift-ed me.... And what His grace can do for you...
2. He saves me from ev-'ry sin and harm,.. Se-cures my soul each day;...... I'm lean-ing strong on His might-y arm;.. I know He'll guide me all the way...
3. When poor and need-y and all a-lone,... In love He said to me,........ "Come un-to me and I'll lead you home, To live with me e-ter-nal-ly."...

CHORUS.

Saved .... by His pow'r di-vine, Saved .... to new life sub-lime!
Saved by His pow'r,              Saved to new life,

*rit.*

Life now is sweet and my joy is com-plete, For I'm Saved, saved, saved!

Copyright, 1911, by Robert H. Coleman

## 11  I Walk With the King

JAMES ROWE  
B. D. ACKLEY

1. In sor-row I wan-dered, my spir-it op-prest, But now I am hap-py—se-cure-ly I rest; From morn-ing till eve-ning glad car-ols I sing, And this is the rea-son—I walk with the King.
2. For years in the fet-ters of sin I was bound, The world could not help me—no com-fort I found; But now like the birds and the sunbeams of spring, I'm free and re-joic-ing—I walk with the King.
3. O soul near de-spair in the low-lands of strife, Look up and let Je-sus come in-to your life; The joy of sal-va-tion to you He would bring—Come in-to the sun-light and walk with the King.

**CHORUS**

I walk with the King, hal-le-lu-jah! I walk with the King, praise His name! No lon-ger I roam, my soul fa-ces home, I walk and I talk with the King.

Copyright, 1915, by Homer A. Rodeheaver. International Copyright secured

## 12 He's a Wonderful Savior to Me

Virgil P. Brock  
Blanche Kerr Brock

1. I was lost in sin but Jesus rescued me, He's a wonderful Savior to me; I was bound by fear but Jesus set me free, He's a wonderful Savior to me.
2. He's a Friend so true, so patient and so kind, He's a wonderful Savior to me; Ev'rything I need in Him I always find, He's a wonderful Savior to me.
3. He is always near to comfort and to cheer, He's a wonderful Savior to me; He forgives my sins, He dries my ev'ry tear, He's a wonderful Savior to me.
4. Dearer grows the love of Jesus day by day, He's a wonderful Savior to me; Sweeter is His grace while pressing on my way, He's a wonderful Savior to me.

**Chorus**

So wonderful! For He's a wonderful Savior to me, He's a wonderful Savior to me; I was lost in sin, but Jesus took me in, He's a wonderful Savior to me.

Copyright, 1918, by Homer A. Rodeheaver. International Copyright secured

# 13. The Way of the Cross Leads Home

JESSIE BROWN POUNDS  
CHAS. H. GABRIEL

1. I must needs go home by the way of the cross, There's no oth-er way but this; I shall ne'er get sight of the Gates of Light, If the way of the cross I miss.
2. I must needs go on in the blood-sprinkled way, The path that the Sav-ior trod, If I ev-er climb to the heights sub-lime, Where the soul is at home with God.
3. Then I bid fare-well to the way of the world, To walk in it nev-er-more; For my Lord says "Come," and I seek my home, Where He waits at the o-pen door.

CHORUS.

The way of the cross leads home, The way of the cross leads home; It is sweet to know, as I on-ward go, The way of the cross leads home. A-MEN.

Copyright, 1906, by Chas. H. Gabriel. Copyright, 1907, by E. O. Excell

# Sweeter As the Years Go By

Mrs. C. H. M. — Mrs. C. H. Morris

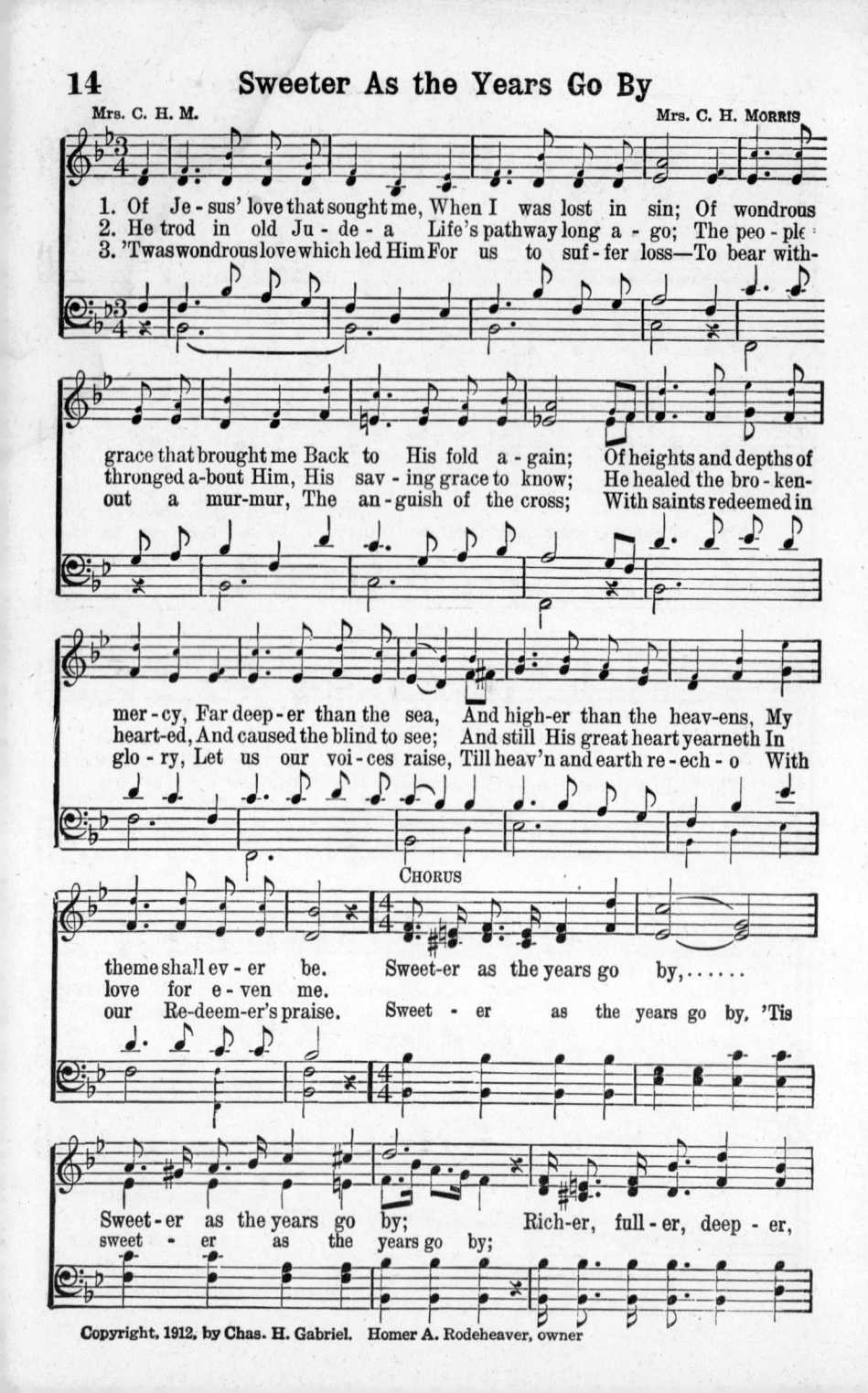

## Sweeter As the Years Go By

Je - sus' love is sweet - er, Sweet - er as the years go by.

## 15     The Victory Side

W. M. R.                                                               WILLIAM M. RUNYAN

1. Tho' foes as-sail us on the field, We will not to their pow-er yield;
2. When test-ings come with-out, with-in, Then, more than conqu'rors o-ver sin,
3. Yes, more than conqu'rors we shall be, The prom-ise stands for you, for me;

Thro' God's own grace to us re-vealed, We're on the vic - t'ry side.
We shall, thro' Christ, the bat - tle win, And find the vic - t'ry side.
From sin's sad bond-age to be free, Oh, find the vic - t'ry side.

**CHORUS**

I am on the vic - t'ry side, Through the grace of Him who died;

I am on the vic - t'ry side, For Je - sus keeps me there!

Copyright, 1925, by W. M. Runyan

## 16    Win Them One by One

C. A. M.  
C. Austin Miles

*In march time*

1. If to Christ our on-ly King Men re-deemed we strive to bring,
2. Side by side we stand each day, Saved are we, but lost are they;
3. On-ly cow-ards dare re-fuse, Dare this gift of God mis-use;
4. Not for hope of great re-ward Turn men's hearts un-to the Lord;

Just one way may this be done—We must win them one by one.
They will come if we but dare Speak a word backed up by prayer.
Ere some friend goes to his grave, Speak a word his soul to save.
Just to see a saved man smile Makes the ef-fort well worth while.

**Chorus**

{ So you bring the one next to you, And I'll bring the one next to me; In
{ If you'll bring the one next to you, And I bring the one next to me, In

all kinds of weather, we'll all work to-geth-er, And see what can be done;

no time at all we'll have them all, So win them, win them one by one.

Copyright, 1915, by Hall-Mack Co. International Copyright secured

## 17 Sail On!

C. H. G.  
Chas. H. Gabriel

**Solo and Chorus**

1. Up-on a wide and storm-y sea, Thou'rt sail-ing to e-ter-ni-ty,
2. Art far from shore, and weary-worn—The sky o'er-cast, thy can-vas torn?
3. Do com-rades trem-ble and re-fuse To fur-ther dare the taunting hues?
4. Do snarl-ing waves thy craft as-sail? Art pow'r-less, drift-ing with the gale?

*ad lib.*

And thy great Ad-m'ral or-ders thee:—"Sail on! sail on! sail on!"
Hark ye! a voice to thee is borne:—"Sail on! sail on! sail on!"
No oth-er course is thine to choose, Sail on! sail on! sail on!
Take heart! God's word shall nev-er fail! Sail on! sail on! sail on!

**Chorus**

Sail on! sail on! the storms will soon be past, The dark-ness will not al-ways last; Sail on! sail on! ...... God lives and He commands: "Sail on! sail on!" ...... sail on! sail on! sail on!

*rit e dim.*  *pp*

\*May close here.

Copyright, 1908, by Chas. H. Gabriel. New arrangement Copyright 1918, by Homer A. Rodeheaver.  
International Copyright secured

## 18 The Ninety and Nine

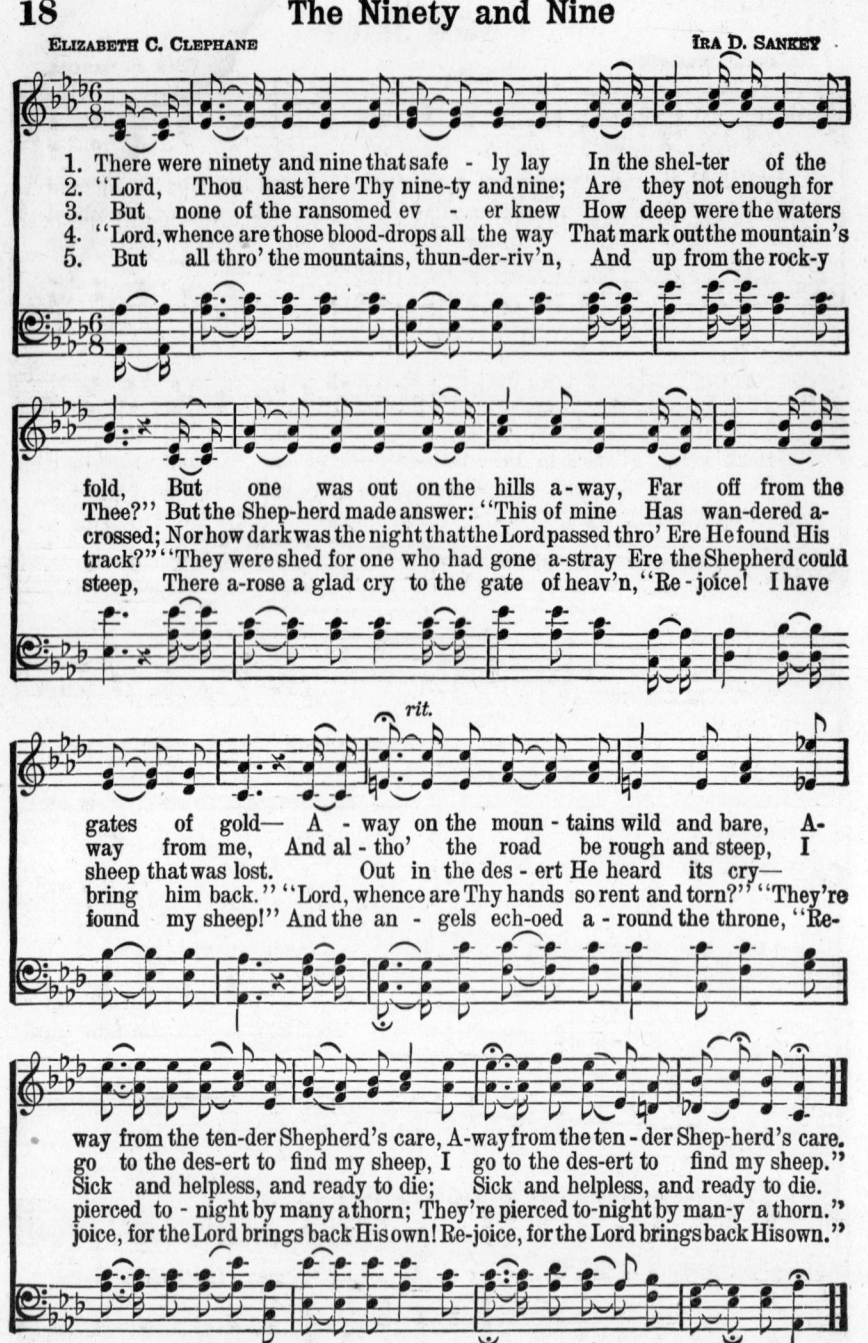

ELIZABETH C. CLEPHANE  
IRA D. SANKEY

1. There were ninety and nine that safe - ly lay In the shel-ter of the
2. "Lord, Thou hast here Thy nine-ty and nine; Are they not enough for
3. But none of the ransomed ev - er knew How deep were the waters
4. "Lord, whence are those blood-drops all the way That mark out the mountain's
5. But all thro' the mountains, thun-der-riv'n, And up from the rock-y

fold, But one was out on the hills a-way, Far off from the
Thee?" But the Shep-herd made answer: "This of mine Has wan-dered a-
crossed; Nor how dark was the night that the Lord passed thro' Ere He found His
track?" "They were shed for one who had gone a-stray Ere the Shepherd could
steep, There a-rose a glad cry to the gate of heav'n, "Re-joice! I have

*rit.*

gates of gold— A - way on the moun - tains wild and bare, A-
way from me, And al - tho' the road be rough and steep, I
sheep that was lost. Out in the des - ert He heard its cry—
bring him back." "Lord, whence are Thy hands so rent and torn?" "They're
found my sheep!" And the an - gels ech-oed a - round the throne, "Re-

way from the ten-der Shepherd's care, A-way from the ten - der Shep-herd's care.
go to the des-ert to find my sheep, I go to the des-ert to find my sheep."
Sick and helpless, and ready to die; Sick and helpless, and ready to die.
pierced to - night by many a thorn; They're pierced to-night by man-y a thorn."
joice, for the Lord brings back His own! Re-joice, for the Lord brings back His own."

Copyright, 1904, Renewal. Hope Publishing Co., owner

## 19     I Need Jesus

GEORGE O. WEBSTER     CHAS. H. GABRIEL

1. I need Jesus, my need I now confess; No friend like Him in times of deep distress; I need Jesus, the need I gladly own; Tho' some may bear their load alone, Yet I need Jesus.
2. I need Jesus, I need a friend like Him, A friend to guide when paths of life are dim; I need Jesus, when foes my soul assail; Alone I know I can but fail, So I need Jesus.
3. I need Jesus, I need Him to the end; No one like Him, He is the sinner's Friend; I need Jesus, no other friend will do; So constant, kind, so strong and true, Yes, I need Jesus.

**CHORUS**

I need Jesus, I need Jesus, I need Jesus with me, I need Jesus always, I need Jesus ev'ry day; . . . Need Him in the sunshine hour, need Him when the storm-clouds low'r; Ev'ry day along my way, Yes, I need Jesus.

Copyright, 1924, by Homer A. Rodeheaver. International Copyright secured

## 20. Is It the Crowning Day?

GEORGE WALKER WHITCOMB  
CHARLES H. MARSH

1. Je-sus may come to-day, Glad day! Glad day! And I would see my Friend; Dan-gers and trou-bles would end If Je-sus should come to-day.
2. I may go home to-day, Glad day! Glad day! Seem-eth I hear their song; Hail to the ra-di-ant throng! If I should go home to-day.
3. Why should I anx-ious be? Glad day! Glad day! Lights ap-pear on the shore, Storms will af-fright nev-er-more, For He is "at hand" to-day.
4. Faithful I'll be to-day, Glad day! Glad day! And I will free-ly tell Why I should love Him so well, For He is my all to-day.

**Chorus**

Glad day! Glad day! Is it the crowning day? I'll live for to-day, nor anx-ious be, Je-sus, my Lord, I soon shall see; Glad day! Glad day! Is it the crown-ing day?

Copyright, 1910, by Praise Publishing Co. Homer A. Rodeheaver, owner

## 21. He Included Me

REV. J. OATMAN, JR.  
HAMP SEWELL

1. I am so hap-py in Christ to-day, That I go sing-ing a-long my way;
2. Glad-ly I read, "Who-so-ev-er may Come to the fountain of life to-day;"
3. Ever God's Spirit is saying, "Come!" Hear the Bride saying, "No longer roam;"
4. "Freely come drink," words the soul to thrill! O with what joy they my heart do fill!

Yes, I'm so hap-py to know and say, "Je-sus in-clud-ed me too."
But when I read it I al-ways say, "Je-sus in-clud-ed me too."
But I am sure while they're calling home, Je-sus in-clud-ed me too.
For when He said, "Who-so-ev-er will," Je-sus in-clud-ed me too.

CHORUS.

Je-sus in-clud-ed me, Yes, He in-clud-ed me, When the Lord said "Who-so-ev-er," He in-clud-ed me; Je-sus in-clud-ed me, Yes, He in-clud-ed me, When the Lord said "Who-so-ev-er," He included me. A-MEN.

Copyright, 1914, by Hamp Sewell. E. O. Excell, owner.

## 22. If Jesus Goes With Me

C. A. M.  
C. Austin Miles

1. It may be in the val-ley, where countless dangers hide; It may be in the sun-shine that I, in peace, a-bide; But this one thing I know—if it be dark or fair, If Je-sus is with me, I'll go an-y-where!

2. It may be I must car-ry the bless-ed word of life A-cross the burning des-erts to those in sin-ful strife; And tho' it be my lot to bear my col-ors there, If Je-sus goes with me, I'll go an-y-where!

3. But if it be my por-tion to bear my cross at home, While others bear their bur-dens be-yond the bil-low's foam, I'll prove my faith in Him—con-fess His judgments fair, And, if He stays with me, I'll stay an-y-where!

4. It is not mine to ques-tion the judg-ments of my Lord, It is but mine to fol-low the lead-ings of His Word; But if to go or stay, or wheth-er here or there, I'll be, with my Sav-ior, Con-tent an-y-where!

**Chorus**

If Je-sus goes with me, I'll go.... An-y-where! 'Tis heaven to me, Wher-e'er I may be, If He is there! I count it a priv-i-lege here.. His cross, His

Copyright, 1908, by Hall-Mack Co.

## If Jesus Goes With Me

cross to bear;.. If Jesus goes with me, I'll go... Anywhere!
cross, His cross to bear;

## 23  I Need Thee Every Hour

Mrs. ANNIE S. HAWKS  
Rev. ROBERT LOWRY

1. I need Thee ev-'ry hour, Most gra-cious Lord; No tender voice like Thine Can peace afford.
2. I need Thee ev-'ry hour, Stay Thou near by; Temp-ta-tions lose their pow'r When Thou art nigh.
3. I need Thee ev-'ry hour, In joy or pain; Come quickly and abide, Or life is vain.
4. I need Thee ev-'ry hour, Most Holy One; O make me Thine indeed, Thou blessed Son!

CHORUS

I need Thee, O I need Thee; Ev-'ry hour I need Thee! O bless me now, my Savior, I come to Thee!

Copyright, 1914, by Mary Runyon Lowry. Renewal. Used by permission

## 24. As a Volunteer

W. S. Brown  
Chas. H. Gabriel

1. A call for loy-al sol-diers Comes to one and all; Sol-diers for the con-flict,
2. Yes, Jesus calls for soldiers Who are filled with pow'r, Soldiers who will serve Him
3. He calls you, for He loves you With a heart most kind, He whose heart was broken,
4. And when the war is o-ver, And the vic-t'ry won, When the true and faith-ful

Will you heed the call! Will you an-swer quick-ly, With a read-y cheer,
Ev-'ry day and hour; He will not for-sake you, He is ev-er near;
Bro-ken for man-kind; Now, just now He calls you, Calls in ac-cents clear,
Gath-er one by one, He will crown with glo-ry All who there ap-pear;

CHORUS.

Will you be en-list-ed As a vol-un-teer? A vol-un-teer for Je-sus, A sol-dier true! Oth-ers have enlisted, Why not you? Je-sus is the Cap-tain, O why not? We will nev-er fear; Will you be en-list-ed As a vol-un-teer? A-MEN.

Copyright, 1907, by Chas. H. Gabriel. E. O. Excell, owner

## 25. Since I Have Been Redeemed

E. O. E.  
E. O. Excell

1. I have a song I love to sing, Since I have been redeemed,
2. I have a Christ that satisfies, Since I have been redeemed,
3. I have a Witness bright and clear, Since I have been redeemed,
4. I have a joy I can't express, Since I have been redeemed,
5. I have a home prepared for me, Since I have been redeemed,

Of my Redeemer, Savior, King, Since I have been redeemed.
To do His will my highest prize, Since I have been redeemed.
Dispelling ev'ry doubt and fear, Since I have been redeemed.
All thro' His blood and righteousness, Since I have been redeemed.
Where I shall dwell eternally, Since I have been redeemed.

**Chorus.**

Since I have been redeemed, Since I have been redeemed, I will glory in His name; Since I have been redeemed, Since I have been redeemed, I will glory in my Savior's name. A-MEN.

Copyright, 1912, by E. O. Excell. Renewal

# 26 Where the Gates Swing Outward Never

C. H. G.  
CHAS. H. GABRIEL

1. Just a few more days to be filled with praise, And to tell the old, old story; Then, when twi-light falls, and my Sav-ior calls, I shall go to Him in glo-ry.
2. Just a few more years with their toil and tears, And the jour-ney will be end-ed; Then I'll be with Him, where the tide of time With e-ter-ni-ty is blend-ed.
3. Tho' the hills be steep and the val-leys deep, With no flow'rs my way a-dorn-ing; Tho' the night be lone and my rest a stone, Joy a-waits me in the morn-ing.
4. What a joy 'twill be when I wake to see Him for whom my heart is burn-ing! Nev-er-more to sigh, nev-er-more to die— For that day my heart is yearn-ing.

**Chorus**

I'll ex-change my cross for a star-ry crown, Where the gates swing out-ward nev-er; At His feet I'll lay ev-'ry bur-den down, And with Je-sus reign for-ev-er.

Copyright, 1920, by Homer A. Rodeheaver. International Copyright secured

## He Lives On High

Words by B. B. McKinney
Arr. by B. B. McKinney
From Hawaiian Folk Song

1. Christ the Sav-ior came from heaven's glo-ry, To re-deem the lost from sin and shame; On His brow He wore the thorn-crown go-ry, And up-on Cal-va-ry He took my blame.
2. He a-rose from death and all its sor-row, To dwell in that land of joy and love; He is com-ing back some glad to-mor-row, And He'll take all His children home a-bove.
3. Wea-ry soul, to Je-sus come con-fess-ing, Re-demp-tion from sin He of-fers thee; Look to Je-sus and re-ceive a bless-ing, There is life, there is joy and vic-to-ry.

**Chorus**

He lives on high, He lives on high, Tri-um-phant o-ver sin and all its stain; He lives on high, He lives on high, Some day He's com-ing a-gain.

Arr. Copyright, 1921, by Robert H. Coleman

# 28. Dwelling in Beulah Land

C. A. M.  
C. Austin Miles

1. Far a-way the noise of strife up-on my ear is fall-ing, Then I know the sins of earth be-set on ev-'ry hand: Doubt and fear and things of earth in vain to me are call-ing, None of these shall move me from Beu-lah Land.

2. Far be-low the storm of doubt up-on the world is beat-ing, Sons of men in bat-tle long the en-e-my with-stand: Safe am I with-in the cas-tle of God's word re-treat-ing, Nothing then can reach me—'tis Beu-lah Land.

3. Let the storm-y breez-es blow, their cry can-not a-larm me; I am safe-ly shel-tered here, pro-tect-ed by God's hand: Here the sun is al-ways shin-ing, here there's naught can harm me, I am safe for-ev-er in Beu-lah Land.

4. Viewing here the works of God, I sink in con-tem-pla-tion, Hearing now His bless-ed voice, I see the way He planned: Dwell-ing in the Spir-it, here I learn of full sal-va-tion, Glad-ly will I tar-ry in Beu-lah Land.

**Chorus**

I'm liv-ing on the moun-tain, un-der-neath a cloud-less sky, (Praise God!) I'm drink-ing at the foun-tain that never shall run dry; O yes! I'm feasting on the

Copyright, 1911, by Hall-Mack Co. International Copyright secured

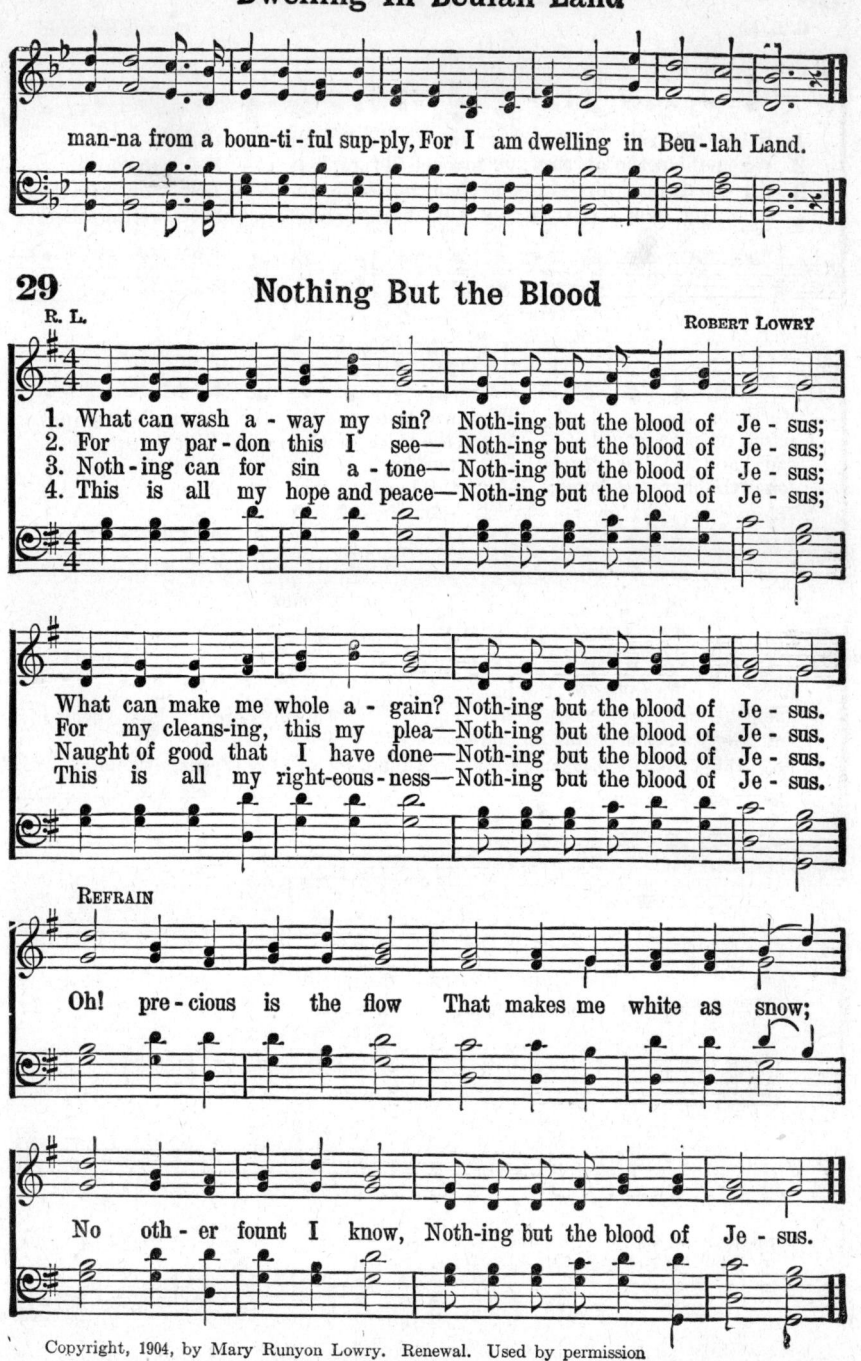

## Dwelling In Beulah Land

man-na from a boun-ti-ful sup-ply, For I am dwelling in Beu-lah Land.

## 29 Nothing But the Blood

R. L.  
ROBERT LOWRY

1. What can wash a-way my sin? Noth-ing but the blood of Je-sus;
2. For my par-don this I see— Noth-ing but the blood of Je-sus;
3. Noth-ing can for sin a-tone— Noth-ing but the blood of Je-sus;
4. This is all my hope and peace— Noth-ing but the blood of Je-sus;

What can make me whole a-gain? Noth-ing but the blood of Je-sus.
For my cleans-ing, this my plea— Noth-ing but the blood of Je-sus.
Naught of good that I have done— Noth-ing but the blood of Je-sus.
This is all my right-eous-ness— Noth-ing but the blood of Je-sus.

REFRAIN

Oh! pre-cious is the flow That makes me white as snow;

No oth-er fount I know, Noth-ing but the blood of Je-sus.

Copyright, 1904, by Mary Runyon Lowry. Renewal. Used by permission

## 30. Speak, My Lord

G. B. — George Bennard

1. Hear the Lord of har-vest sweet-ly call-ing, "Who will go and work for Me to-day? Who will bring to Me the lost and dy-ing? Who will point them to the nar-row way?"
2. When the coal of fire... touched the proph-et, Mak-ing him as pure, as pure can be; When the voice of God said, "Who'll go for us?" Then he an-swered, "Here I am, send me."
3. Mil-lions now in sin and shame are dy-ing; Lis-ten to their sad and bit-ter cry; Has-ten, broth-er, has-ten to the res-cue; Quick-ly an-swer, "Mas-ter, here am I."
4. Soon the time for reap-ing will be o-ver; Soon we'll gath-er for the har-vest-home; May the Lord of har-vest smile up-on us, May we hear His bless-ed, "Child, well done."

CHORUS

Speak, my Lord, speak, my Lord, Speak, and I'll be quick to an-swer Thee; Speak, my Lord, speak, my Lord, Speak, and I will answer, "Lord, send me."

Copyright, 1911, by Geo. Bennard

# 31 There is Power in the Blood

L. E. J.  
L. E. Jones

1. Would you be free from the bur-den of sin? There's pow'r in the blood, pow'r in the blood; Would you o'er e-vil a vic-to-ry win? There's
2. Would you be free from your pas-sion and pride? There's pow'r in the blood, pow'r in the blood; Come for a cleans-ing to Cal-va-ry's tide; There's
3. Would you be whit-er, much whiter than snow? There's pow'r in the blood, pow'r in the blood; Sin-stains are lost in its life-giv-ing flow; There's
4. Would you do serv-ice for Je-sus your King? There's pow'r in the blood, pow'r in the blood; Would you live dai-ly His prais-es to sing? There's

**Chorus.**

won-der-ful pow'r in the blood. There is pow'r, pow'r, Wonder-working pow'r In the blood of the Lamb; There is pow'r, pow'r, Won-der-work-ing pow'r In the pre-cious blood of the Lamb. A-MEN.

Copyright, 1899, by H. L. Gilmour, Wenonah, N. J. Used by permission

## 32. I Know Whom I Have Believed

El Nathan
Moderato

James McGranahan

1. I know not why God's won-drous grace To me He hath made known,
2. I know not how this sav-ing faith To me He did im-part,
3. I know not how the Spir-it moves, Con-vinc-ing men of sin,
4. I know not what of good or ill May be re-served for me,
5. I know not when my Lord may come, At night or noon-day fair,

Nor why un-wor-thy—Christ in love Re-deemed me for His own.
Nor how be-liev-ing in His Word Wrought peace within my heart.
Re-veal-ing Je-sus thro' the Word, Cre-at-ing faith in Him.
Of wea-ry ways or gold-en days, Be-fore His face I see.
Nor if I walk the vale with Him, Or "meet Him in the air."

**Chorus**

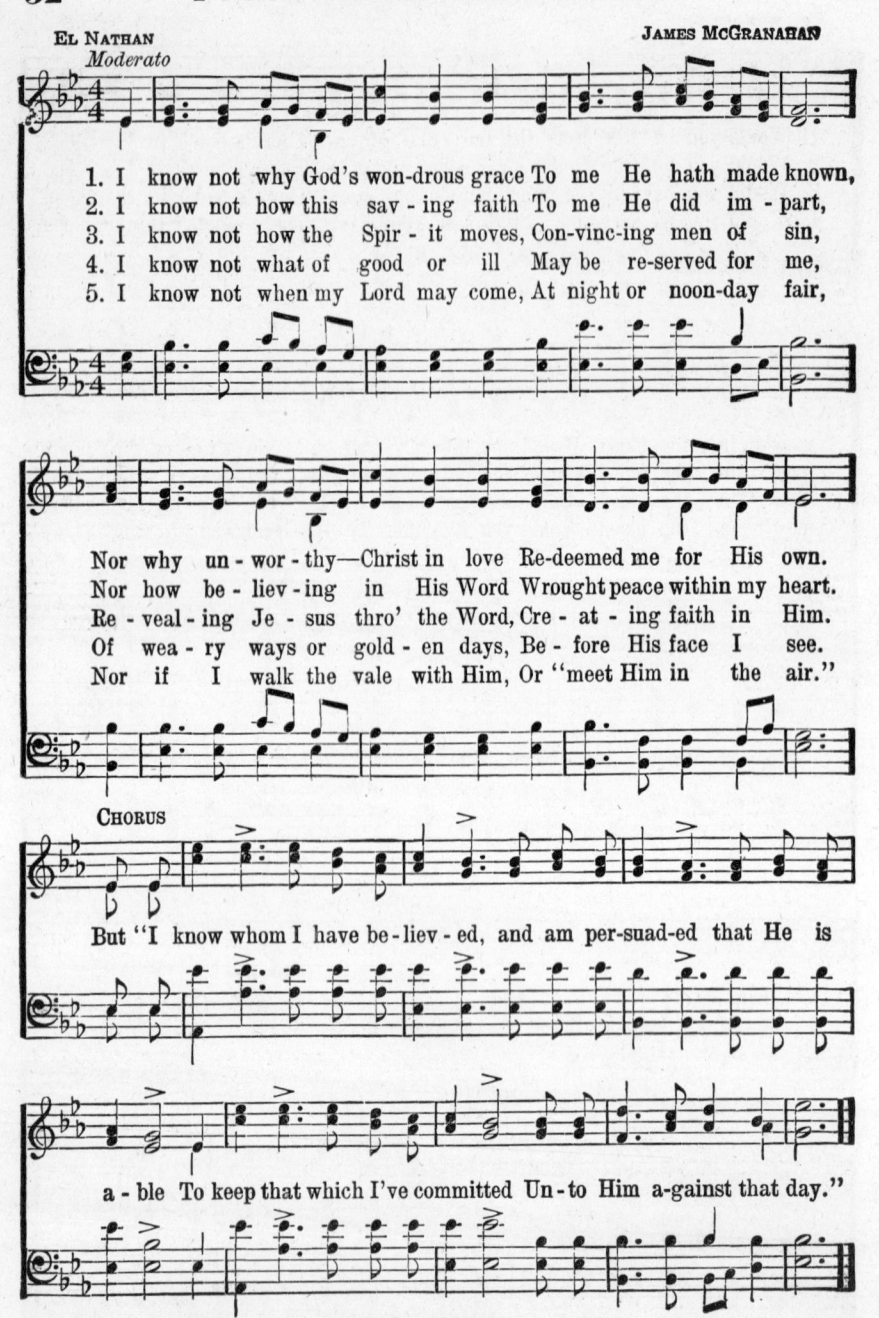

But "I know whom I have be-liev-ed, and am per-suad-ed that He is a-ble To keep that which I've committed Un-to Him a-gainst that day."

Copyright, 1913, Renewal. Hope Publishing Co., owner

## 33 Saved By the Blood

S. J. Henderson  
D. B. Towner

1. Saved by the blood of the Cru-ci-fied One! Ran-somed from sin and a new work be-gun, Sing praise to the Fa-ther and praise to the Son, Saved by the blood of the Cru-ci-fied One!
2. Saved by the blood of the Cru-ci-fied One! The an-gels re-joic-ing be-cause it is done; A child of the Fa-ther, joint-heir with the Son, Saved by the blood of the Cru-ci-fied One!
3. Saved by the blood of the Cru-ci-fied One! The Fa-ther He spake, and His will it was done; Great price of my par-don, His own pre-cious Son; Saved by the blood of the Cru-ci-fied One!
4. Saved by the blood of the Cru-ci-fied One! All hail to the Fa-ther, all hail to the Son, All hail to the Spir-it, the great Three in One! Saved by the blood of the Cru-ci-fied One!

**Chorus**

Saved!.. saved!.. My sins are all pardoned my guilt is all gone!  
Glo-ry, I'm saved! glo-ry, I'm saved!  
Saved!.. saved!.. I am saved by the blood of the Cru-ci-fied One!  
Glo-ry, I'm saved! glo-ry, I'm saved!

Copyright, 1903. Hope Publishing Co., owner

## 34. He Ransomed Me

JULIA H. JOHNSTON  
J. W. HENDERSON

1. There's a sweet and bless-ed sto-ry Of the Christ who came from glo-ry,
2. From the depth of sin and sad-ness To the heights of joy and glad-ness
3. From the throne of heav'n-ly glo-ry—Oh, the sweet and bless-ed sto-ry!
4. By and by with joy in-creas-ing, And with grat-i-tude un-ceas-ing,

Just to res-cue me from sin and mis-er-y; He in loving kindness sought me,
Je-sus lift-ed me, in mer-cy full and free; With His precious blood He bo't me,
Je-sus came to lift the lost in sin and woe In-to lib-er-ty all-glo-rious,
Lift-ed up with Christ for-ev-er-more to be; I will join the hosts there sing-ing,

*ad lib.*

And from sin and shame hath bro't me, Hal-le-lu-jah! Je-sus ran-somed me.
When I knew Him not, He sought me, And in love di-vine He ran-somed me.
Tro-phies of His grace vic-to-rious, Ev-er-more re-joic-ing here be-low.
In the an-them ev-er ring-ing, To the King of Love who ran-somed me.

**CHORUS**

Hal-le-lu-jah, what a Sav-ior! Who can take a poor lost sin-ner, Lift him

from the mi-ry clay and set him free; (Hal-le-lu-jah!) I will ev-er tell the sto-ry,

Copyright, 1916, by Homer A. Hammontree

## He Ransomed Me

Shout-ing glo - ry, glo - ry, glo - ry, Hal - le - lu - jah! Je - sus ran - somed me.

## 35. Leaning On the Everlasting Arms

E. A. Hoffman  
A. J. Showalter

1. What a fel-low-ship, what a joy di-vine, Leaning on the ev-er-last-ing arms;
2. Oh, how sweet to walk in this pilgrim way, Leaning on the ev-er-last-ing arms;
3. What have I to dread, what have I to fear, Leaning on the ev-er-last-ing arms?

What a bless-ed-ness, what a peace is mine, Leaning on the ev-er-last-ing arms.
Oh, how bright the path grows from day to day, Leaning on the ev-er-last-ing arms.
I have bless-ed peace with my Lord so near, Leaning on the ev-er-last-ing arms.

**Refrain**

Lean - ing, lean - ing, Safe and se-cure from all a-larms;
Lean-ing on Je-sus, lean-ing on Je-sus,

Lean - ing, lean - ing, Lean-ing on the ev-er-last-ing arms.
Lean-ing on Je-sus, lean-ing on Je-sus,

By permission of A. J. Showalter.

## 36 Love Found a Way

Constance B. Ried  
Harry Dixon Loes

1. Won-der-ful love that res-cued me, Sunk deep in sin, Guilt-y and vile as I could be—No hope with-in; When ev-'ry ray of light had fled, O glo-rious day! Rais-ing my soul from out the dead, Love found a way.
2. Love bro't my Sav-ior here to die On Cal-va-ry, For such a sin-ful wretch as I, How can it be? Love bridged the gulf 'twixt me and heav'n, Taught me to pray; I am redeemed, set free, for-giv'n, Love found a way.
3. Love o-pened wide the gates of light To heav'n's do-main, Where in e-ter-nal pow'r and might Je-sus shall reign; Love lift-ed me from depths of woe To end-less day, There was no help in earth be-low, Love found a way.

**Chorus**

Love found a way . . to re-deem my soul, . . Love found a way . . . that could make me whole; . . Love sent my Lord . . to the

a way, to re-deem my soul, a way could make me whole; my Lord

Copyright, 1921. Hope Publishing Co., owner

## Love Found a Way

*ad lib.*

cross of shame, Love found a way, O praise His ho-ly name!
to the cross of shame,

---

### 37. Just a Little Help From You

Maud Frazer Jackson  
Geo. C. Stebbins

1. Do you ev-er stop, my friend, to think, The while this world you're passing thro',
2. Just a lit-tle deed of kind-ness now, It may the faith of one re-store,
3. Just a lit-tle word of Je-sus' love, Some precious soul may help de-cide
4. Let us do our part, ere day is done, And to our call-ing faith-ful be;

Some-one may be saved from ruin's brink, By just a lit-tle help from you?
Who beneath some load of grief doth bow, Is al-most read-y to give o'er.
To for-sake the wrong and look a-bove, And let the Lord his foot-steps guide.
For the world to Christ must now be won, By help of you, by help of me.

**Chorus**

Just a lit-tle help from you, . . . . Just a lit-tle help from you; . . . .
Just a little help from you, Just a little help from you;

Won-drous things the Lord may do, By just a lit-tle help from you.

Copyright, 1915. Hope Publishing Co., owner

## 38  I Would Be Like Jesus

JAMES ROWE  B. D. ACKLEY

1. Earth-ly pleas-ures vain-ly call me; I would be like Je-sus;
2. He has bro-ken ev-'ry fet-ter, I would be like Je-sus;
3. All the way from earth to Glo-ry, I would be like Je-sus;
4. That in Heav-en He may meet me, I would be like Je-sus;

would be like Je-sus;

Noth-ing world-ly shall en-thrall me; I would be like Je-sus.
That my soul may serve Him bet-ter, I would be like Je-sus.
Tell-ing o'er and o'er the sto-ry, I would be like Je-sus.
That His words "Well done" may greet me, I would be like Je-sus.

would be like Je-sus.

CHORUS.

Be like Je-sus, this my song, In the home and in the throng;

Be like Je-sus, all day long! I would be like Je-sus. A-MEN.

Copyright, 1911, by E. O. Excell. Words and Music

## 39. My Savior's Love

C. H. G.                                                                        Chas. H Gabriel

1. I stand a-mazed in the pres-ence Of Je-sus the Naz-a-rene,
2. For me it was in the gar-den He prayed: "Not My will, but Thine;"
3. In pit-y an-gels be-held Him, And came from the world of light
4. He took my sins and my sor-rows, He made them His ver-y own;
5. When with the ransomed in glo-ry His face I at last shall see,

And won-der how He could love me, A sin-ner, condemned, un-clean.
He had no tears for His own griefs, But sweat-drops of blood for mine.
To com-fort Him in the sor-rows He bore for my soul that night.
He bore the bur-den to Cal-v'ry, And suf-fered, and died a-lone.
'Twill be my joy thro' the a-ges To sing of His love for me.

**Chorus.**

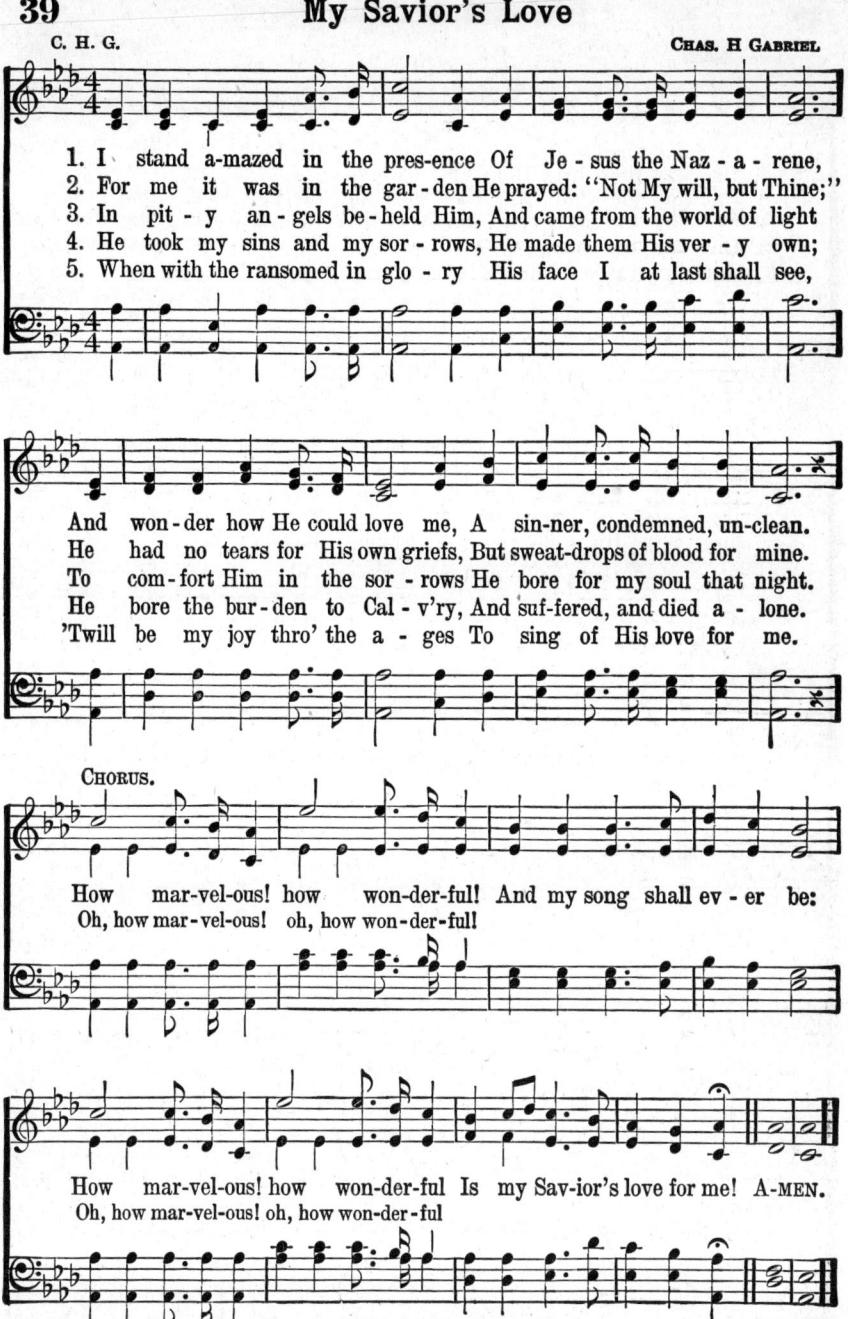

How mar-vel-ous! how won-der-ful! And my song shall ev-er be:
Oh, how mar-vel-ous! oh, how won-der-ful!

How mar-vel-ous! how won-der-ful Is my Sav-ior's love for me! A-men.
Oh, how mar-vel-ous! oh, how won-der-ful

Copyright, 1905, Hope Publishing Co., owner

# One Day!

Rev. J. Wilbur Chapman, D.D.  
Chas. H. Marsh

1. One day when heav-en was filled with His prais-es, One day when sin was as black as could be,... Je-sus came forth to be born of a vir-gin—Dwelt amongst men, my ex-am-ple is He!...
2. One day they led Him up Cal-va-ry's moun-tain, One day they nailed Him to die on the tree;.. Suf-fer-ing an-guish, de-spised and re-ject-ed: Bear-ing our sins, my Re-deem-er is He!...
3. One day they left Him a-lone in the gar-den, One day He rest-ed, from suf-fer-ing free;.. An-gels came down o'er His tomb to keep vig-il; Hope of the hope-less, my Sav-ior is He!...
4. One day the grave could con-ceal Him no lon-ger, One day the stone rolled a-way from the door;. Then He a-rose, o-ver death He had con-quered; Now is as-cend-ed, my Lord ev-er-more!.
5. One day the trump-et will sound for His com-ing, One day the skies with His glo-ries will shine; Won-der-ful day, my be-lov-ed ones bring-ing; Glo-ri-ous Sav-ior, this Je-sus is mine!.

**Chorus**

Liv-ing, He loved me; dy-ing, He saved me; Bur-ied, He car-ried my sins far a-way;.. Ris-ing, He jus-ti-fied

Copyright, 1910. Hope Publishing Co., owner

## One Day!

free-ly for-ev-er: One day He's com-ing—O glo-ri-ous day!

### 41. Take Time to Be Holy

W. D. LONGSTAFF  
GEO. C. STEBBINS

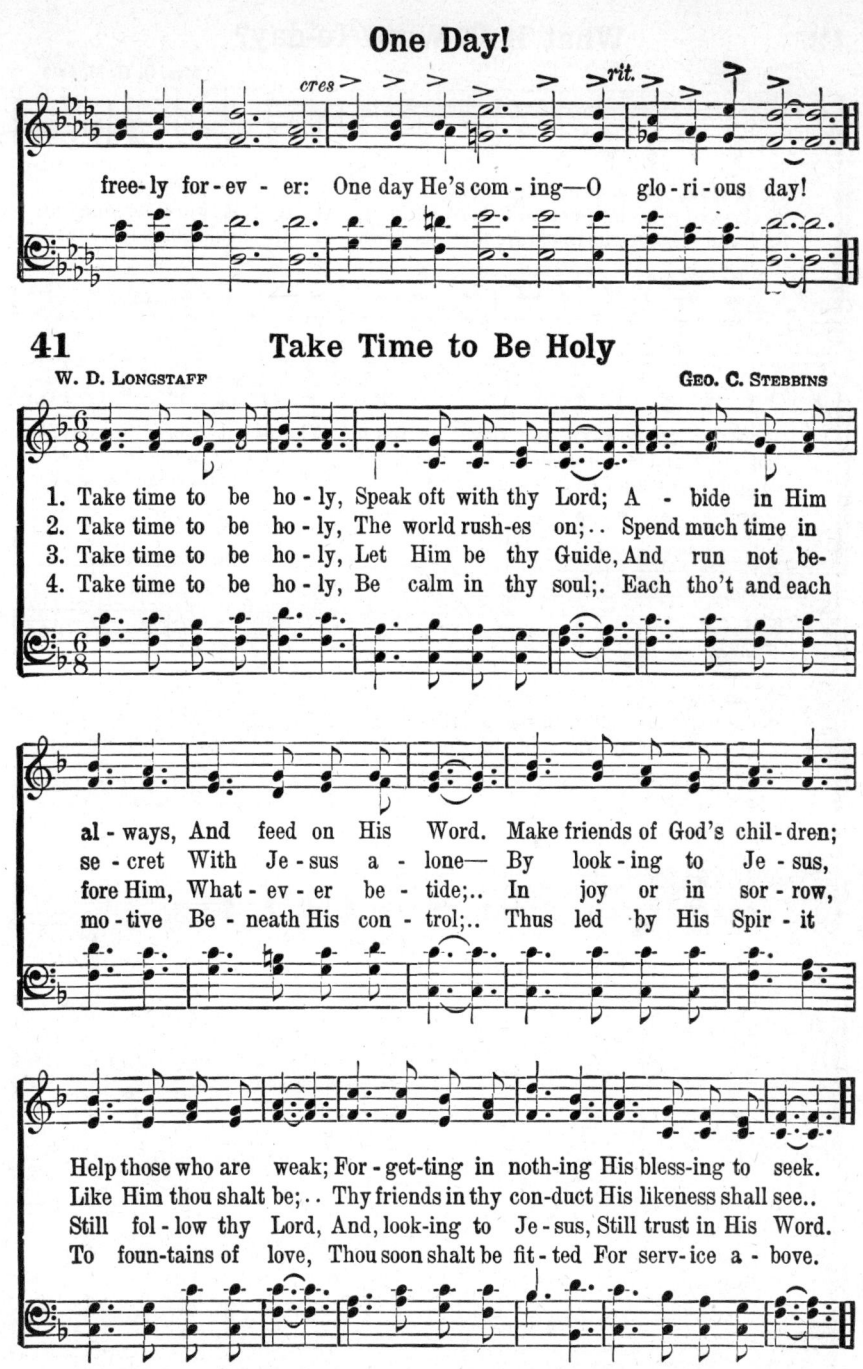

1. Take time to be ho-ly, Speak oft with thy Lord; A-bide in Him al-ways, And feed on His Word. Make friends of God's chil-dren; Help those who are weak; For-get-ting in noth-ing His bless-ing to seek.
2. Take time to be ho-ly, The world rush-es on;.. Spend much time in se-cret With Je-sus a-lone— By look-ing to Je-sus, Like Him thou shalt be;.. Thy friends in thy con-duct His likeness shall see..
3. Take time to be ho-ly, Let Him be thy Guide, And run not be-fore Him, What-ev-er be-tide;.. In joy or in sor-row, Still fol-low thy Lord, And, look-ing to Je-sus, Still trust in His Word.
4. Take time to be ho-ly, Be calm in thy soul;. Each tho't and each mo-tive Be-neath His con-trol;.. Thus led by His Spir-it To foun-tains of love, Thou soon shalt be fit-ted For serv-ice a-bove.

Copyright, 1918, by Geo. C. Stebbins. Renewal. Hope Publishing Company, owner

## 42. What If It Were To-day?

Mrs. C. H. M.  
Mrs. C. H. Morris

1. Je-sus is com-ing to earth a-gain, What if it were to-day?
2. Sa-tan's do-min-ion will then be o'er, O that it were to-day!
3. Faith-ful and true would He find us here If He should come to-day?

Com-ing in pow-er and love to reign, What if it were to-day?
Sor-row and sigh-ing shall be no more, O that it were to-day!
Watching in glad-ness and not in fear, If He should come to-day?

Com-ing to claim His cho-sen Bride, All the re-deemed and pu-ri-fied,
Then shall the dead in Christ a-rise, Caught up to meet Him in the skies,
Signs of His com-ing mul-ti-ply, Morning light breaks in east-ern sky,

*rit.* *a tempo*

O-ver this whole earth scat-tered wide, What if it were to-day?
When shall these glo-ries meet our eyes? What if it were to-day?
Watch, for the time is draw-ing nigh, What if it were to-day?

**Chorus**

Glo-ry, glo-ry! Joy to my heart 'twill bring;.. Glo-ry, glo-ry!
Joy to my heart 'twill bring;

Copyright, 1912, by Wm. J. Kirkpatrick. Hope Publishing Co., owner

## What If It Were To-day?

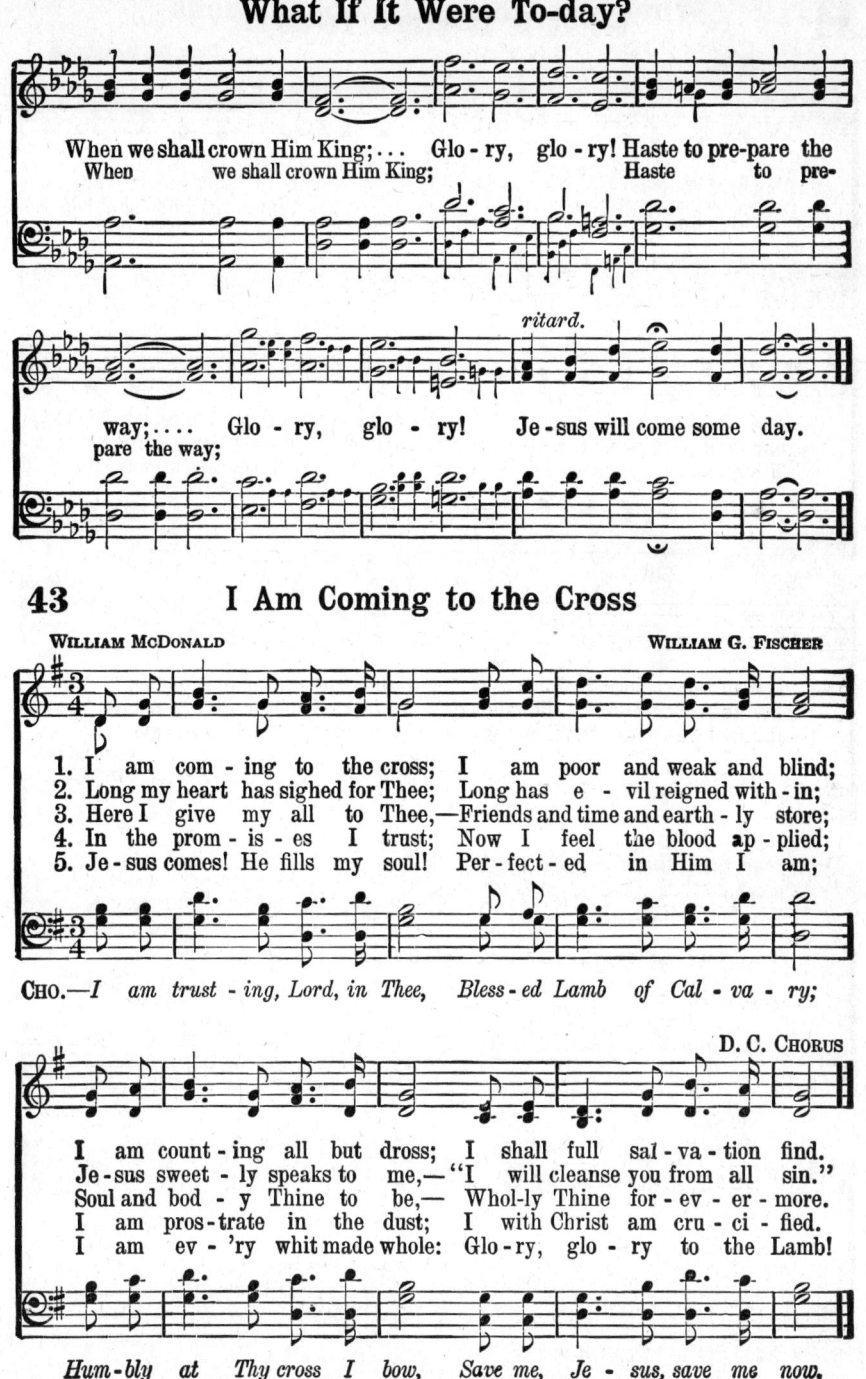

When we shall crown Him King;... Glo-ry, glo-ry! Haste to pre-pare the
When we shall crown Him King; Haste to pre-

way;... Glo-ry, glo-ry! Je-sus will come some day.
pare the way;

## 43  I Am Coming to the Cross

WILLIAM McDONALD                    WILLIAM G. FISCHER

1. I am com-ing to the cross; I am poor and weak and blind;
2. Long my heart has sighed for Thee; Long has e-vil reigned with-in;
3. Here I give my all to Thee,—Friends and time and earth-ly store;
4. In the prom-is-es I trust; Now I feel the blood ap-plied;
5. Je-sus comes! He fills my soul! Per-fect-ed in Him I am;

CHO.—I am trust-ing, Lord, in Thee, Bless-ed Lamb of Cal-va-ry;

D. C. CHORUS

I am count-ing all but dross; I shall full sal-va-tion find.
Je-sus sweet-ly speaks to me,— "I will cleanse you from all sin."
Soul and bod-y Thine to be,— Whol-ly Thine for-ev-er-more.
I am pros-trate in the dust; I with Christ am cru-ci-fied.
I am ev-'ry whit made whole: Glo-ry, glo-ry to the Lamb!

Hum-bly at Thy cross I bow, Save me, Je-sus, save me now.

# 44 When They Ring the Golden Bells

DION DE MARBELLE

1. There's a land be-yond the riv-er, That we call the sweet for-ev-er, And we on-ly reach that shore by faith's decree; One by one we'll gain the portals, There to dwell with the immortals, When they ring the golden bells for you and me.
2. We shall know no sin nor sor-row, In that ha-ven of to-mor-row, When our barque shall sail beyond the sil-ver sea; We shall on-ly know the blessing Of our Father's sweet caressing, When they ring the golden bells for you and me.
3. When our days shall know their number, When in death we sweetly slumber, When the King commands the spir-it to be free; Nevermore with anguish la-den, We shall reach that love-ly ai-den, When they ring the golden bells for you and me.

D. S.—yond the shining riv-er, When they ring the gold-en bells for you and me.

CHORUS

Don't you hear the bells now ringing? Don't you hear the an-gels singing? 'Tis the glo-ry hal-le-lu-jah Ju-bi-lee. (Ju-bi-lee.) In that far-off sweet for-ev-er, Just be-

Copyright, 1887, by Dion De Marbelle,

## 45     A Great Salvation

Avis B. Christiansen                                                 Harry Dixon Loes

1. 'Tis a great sal-va-tion that hath reached my soul, 'Tis a great sal-va-tion that hath made me whole; Jesus' blood hath set me free, I am saved e-ter-nal-ly, Saved by grace di-vine.
2. 'Tis a great sal-va-tion that could cleanse my heart, Wondrous pow'r that bade my ev-'ry sin de-part! On-ly trust-ing in His name, With my guilt-y soul I came, And He par-doned me.
3. 'Tis a great sal-va-tion, sav-ing such as I; 'Tis a won-drous Sav-ior that hath brought it nigh; Oh, how could I si-lent be, When I'm ran-somed and set free For e-ter-ni-ty!

**Chorus**

'Tis a { great sal-va-tion, a great sal-va-tion,—From sin and con-dem-na-tion it sets me free; 'Tis a }
{ great sal-va-tion, a great sal-va-tion, Its bless-ed "who-so-ev-er" (*Omit.*). . . . . . . . . . } in-clud-ed me!

Copyright, 1925, by Federation Publishing Co.

# 46. Saved!

Rev. Oswald J. Smith
Rodger M. Hickman

1. Saved! saved! saved! my sins are all for-giv'n; Christ is mine! I'm on my way to heav'n; Once a guilty sinner, lost, un-done, Now a child of God, saved thro' His Son.
2. Saved! saved! saved! by grace and grace a-lone; Oh, what wondrous love to me was shown, In my stead Christ Jesus bled and died, Bore my sins, for me was cru-ci-fied.
3. Saved! saved! saved! oh, joy be-yond com-pare; Christ my life, and I His con-stant care, Yield-ing all and trust-ing Him a-lone, Liv-ing now each moment as His own.

**Chorus**

Saved! I'm saved thro' Christ, my all in all; .... Saved! I'm saved, what-ever may be-fall; He died up-on the cross for me, He bore the aw-ful

Copyright, 1918. Hope Publishing Co., owner

## Saved!

*rit.*

pen-al-ty; And now I'm saved e-ter-nal-ly—I'm saved! saved! saved!

## 47  When We All Get to Heaven

E. E. Hewitt  
Mrs. J. G. Wilson

1. Sing the won-drous love of Je-sus, Sing His mer-cy and His grace;
2. While we walk the pil-grim pathway, Clouds will o-ver-spread the sky;
3. Let us then be true and faith-ful, Trust-ing, serv-ing ev-'ry day;
4. On-ward to the prize be-fore us! Soon His beau-ty we'll be-hold;

In the man-sions bright and blessed, He'll pre-pare for us a place.
But when trav'ling days are o-ver, Not a shad-ow, not a sigh.
Just one glimpse of Him in glo-ry Will the toils of life re-pay.
Soon the pearl-y gates will o-pen, We shall tread the streets of gold.

for us a place.

**Chorus**

When we all get to heaven, What a day of re-joicing that will be!
When we all       What a day of re-joicing that will be!

When we all see Je-sus, We'll sing and shout the vic-to-ry.........
When we all            and shout the vic-to-ry.

Copyright, 1898, by Mrs. J. G. Wilson

## 48. My Redeemer

P. P. Bliss
James McGranahan

1. I will sing of my Redeemer, And His wondrous love to me;
On the cruel cross He suffered, From the curse to set me free.

2. I will tell the wondrous story, How my lost estate to save,
In His boundless love and mercy, He the ransom freely gave.

3. I will praise my dear Redeemer, His triumphant pow'r I'll tell,
How the victory He giveth Over sin, and death, and hell.

4. I will sing of my Redeemer, And His heav'nly love to me;
He from death to life hath bro't me, Son of God with Him to be.

CHORUS

Sing, oh, sing of my Redeemer,
of my Redeemer, Sing, oh, sing of my Redeemer,
With His blood He purchased me,
He purchased me, With His blood He purchased me,
On the cross He sealed my pardon,
He sealed my pardon, On the cross He sealed my pardon,

Copyright, 1906, Renewal. Hope Publishing Co., owner

## My Redeemer

Paid the debt, ........ and made me free. ........
and made me free,
and made me free.

---

## 49  Take the Name of Jesus With You

Mrs. Lydia Baxter  
W. H. Doane

1. Take the name of Je-sus with you, Child of sor-row and of woe;
2. Take the name of Je-sus ev - er, As a shield from ev-'ry snare;
3. O the precious name of Je - sus! How it thrills our souls with joy,
4. At the name of Je - sus bow-ing, Fall-ing pros-trate at His feet,

It will joy and com-fort give you, Take it, then, wher-e'er you go.
If temp-ta-tions round you gath-er, Breathe that ho - ly name in prayer.
When His lov-ing arms re-ceive us, And His songs our tongues em-ploy!
King of kings in Heav'n we'll crown Him, When our jour-ney is com-plete.

**Chorus**

Pre-cious name, O how sweet! Hope of earth and joy of Heav'n;
Precious name, O how sweet!

Pre-cious name, O how sweet!... Hope of earth and joy of Heav'n.
Precious name, O how sweet, how sweet!

Copyright, 1899, by W. H. Doane. Renewal

# 50 Christ Receiveth Sinful Men

Arr. from NEUMASTER, 1671
JAMES McGRANAHAN

1. Sin-ners Je-sus will re-ceive; Sound this word of grace to all
2. Come, and He will give you rest; Trust Him, for His word is plain;
3. Now my heart con-demns me not, Pure be-fore the law I stand;
4. Christ re-ceiv-eth sin-ful men, E-ven me with all my sin;

Who the heav'n-ly path-way leave, All who lin-ger, all who fall.
He will take the sin-ful-est; Christ re-ceiv-eth sin-ful men.
He who cleansed me from all spot, Sat-is-fied its last de-mand.
Purged from ev-'ry spot and stain, Heav'n with Him I en-ter in.

REFRAIN

Sing it o'er...... and o'er a-gain;...... Christ re-
Sing it o'er a-gain, Sing it o'er a-gain; Christ re-

ceiv---eth sin-ful men;...... Make the mes---sage
ceiv-eth sin-ful men, Christ re-ceiv-eth sin-ful men; Make the message plain,

clear and plain:...... Christ re-ceiv-eth sin-ful men.
Make the mes-sage plain:

Copyright, 1910, Renewal. Hope Publishing Co., owner

# Christ Returneth

H. L. Turner  
James McGranahan

1. It may be at morn, when the day is a-wak-ing, When sunlight thro' dark-ness and shad-ow is break-ing, That Je-sus will come in the full-ness of glo-ry, To re-ceive from the world "His own."

2. It may be at mid-day, it may be at twi-light, It may be, per-chance, that the black-ness of mid-night Will burst in-to light in the blaze of His glo-ry, When Je-sus re-ceives "His own."

3. While its hosts cry Hosanna, from heaven de-scend-ing, With glo-ri-fied saints and the an-gels at-tend-ing, With grace on His brow, like a ha-lo of glo-ry, Will Je-sus re-ceive "His own."

4. Oh, joy! oh, de-light! should we go with-out dy-ing, No sick-ness, no sad-ness, no dread and no cry-ing, Caught up thro' the clouds with our Lord in-to glo-ry, When Je-sus re-ceives "His own."

**Chorus**

O Lord Je-sus, how long, how long Ere we shout the glad song, Christ re-turn-eth! Hal-le-lu-jah! hal-le-lu-jah! A-men, Hal-le-lu-jah! A-men.

Copyright, 1906, Renewal. Hope Publishing Co., owner

# 52 There Shall Be Showers of Blessing

EL NATHAN  
JAMES McGRANAHAN

1. "There shall be show-ers of bless-ing:" This is the prom-ise of love;
2. "There shall be show-ers of bless-ing"—Pre-cious re-viv-ing a-gain;
3. "There shall be show-ers of bless-ing:" Send them up-on us, O Lord;
4. "There shall be show-ers of bless-ing:" Oh, that to-day they might fall,

There shall be sea-sons re-fresh-ing, Sent from the Sav-ior a-bove.
O-ver the hills and the val-leys, Sound of a-bun-dance of rain.
Grant to us now a re-fresh-ing, Come, and now hon-or Thy Word.
Now as to God we're con-fess-ing, Now as on Je-sus we call!

**CHORUS**

Show — — ers of bless-ing, Show-ers of bless-ing we need:
Show-ers, show-ers of bless-ing,

Mer-cy-drops round us are fall-ing, But for the show-ers we plead.

Copyright, 1921, Renewal. Hope Publishing Co., owner

## 53  On the Homeward Way

WILLIAM M. RUNYAN  ETHEL M. MCKEE

1. I am on the heav'n-ly high-way, With the Sav-ior as my guide;
2. When He speaks temptations leave me, At His word my sor-rows cease;
3. Hour by hour I know Him near me, And His praise I glad-ly sing;
4. There is bless-ing for the jour-ney, There is grace for ev-'ry day;

O, 'tis sweet to feel His pres-ence, For He's walk-ing by my side.
From the woes of life that grieve me Je-sus gives me sweet re-lease.
Heav'n-ly grace and mer-cy cheer me On the high-way of my King.
Turn-ing from all sin and fol-ly Seek the bless-ed home-ward way!

CHORUS

On the home — ward way with the King, On the home — ward way;
On the home-ward way with the King, On the bless-ed home-ward way;

How my heart with joy is sing-ing On the home — ward way.
On the bless-ed home-ward way.

Copyright, 1925, by W. M. Runyan

## 54. My Anchor Holds

W. C. Martin, arr.  
D. B. Towner

1. Tho' the an-gry sur-ges roll On my tem-pest-driv-en soul,
2. Might-y tides a-bout me sweep, Per-ils lurk with-in the deep,
3. I can feel the an-chor fast As I meet each sud-den blast,
4. Troub-les al-most 'whelm the soul; Griefs like bil-lows o'er me roll;

I am peace-ful, for I know, Wild-ly though the winds may blow,
An-gry clouds o'er-shade the sky, And the tem-pest ris-es high;
And the ca-ble, though un-seen, Bears the heav-y strain be-tween;
Tempters seek to lure a-stray; Storms ob-scure the light of day:

I've an an-chor safe and sure, That can ev-er-more en-dure.
Still I stand the tem-pest's shock, For my an-chor grips the Rock.
Thro' the storm I safe-ly ride, Till the turn-ing of the tide.
But in Christ I can be bold, I've an an-chor that shall hold.

**Chorus**

And it holds, my an-chor holds; Blow your wild-est, then, O
And it holds,...... my an-chor holds; Blow your wild - - - est,

gale, On my bark so small and frail: By His grace I shall not
then, O gale,

Copyright, 1902–1910. Hope Publishing Co., owner

## My Anchor Holds

fail, For my an - chor holds, my an - chor holds.
For my an - chor holds, it firm - ly holds,

## 55  Sweet Hour of Prayer

W. W. WALFORD  
WM. B. BRADBURY

1. Sweet hour of prayer! sweet hour of prayer! That calls me from a world of care,
2. Sweet hour of prayer! sweet hour of prayer! Thy wings shall my pe - ti - tion bear
3. Sweet hour of prayer! sweet hour of prayer! May I thy con - so - la - tion share,

And bids me at my Fa - ther's throne Make all my wants and wish - es known;
To Him whose truth and faith-ful-ness En - gage the wait-ing soul to bless;
Till, from Mount Pisgah's loft - y height, I view my home, and take my flight:

In sea - sons of dis-tress and grief, My soul has oft - en found re - lief,
And since He bids me seek His face, Be-lieve His word and trust His grace,
This robe of flesh I'll drop, and rise To seize the ev - er - last - ing prize;

And oft es - caped the tempter's snare By thy re-turn, sweet hour of prayer.
I'll cast on Him my ev - 'ry care, And wait for thee, sweet hour of prayer.
And shout, while passing thro' the air, Farewell, farewell, sweet hour of prayer.

## 56. He Will Hold Me Fast

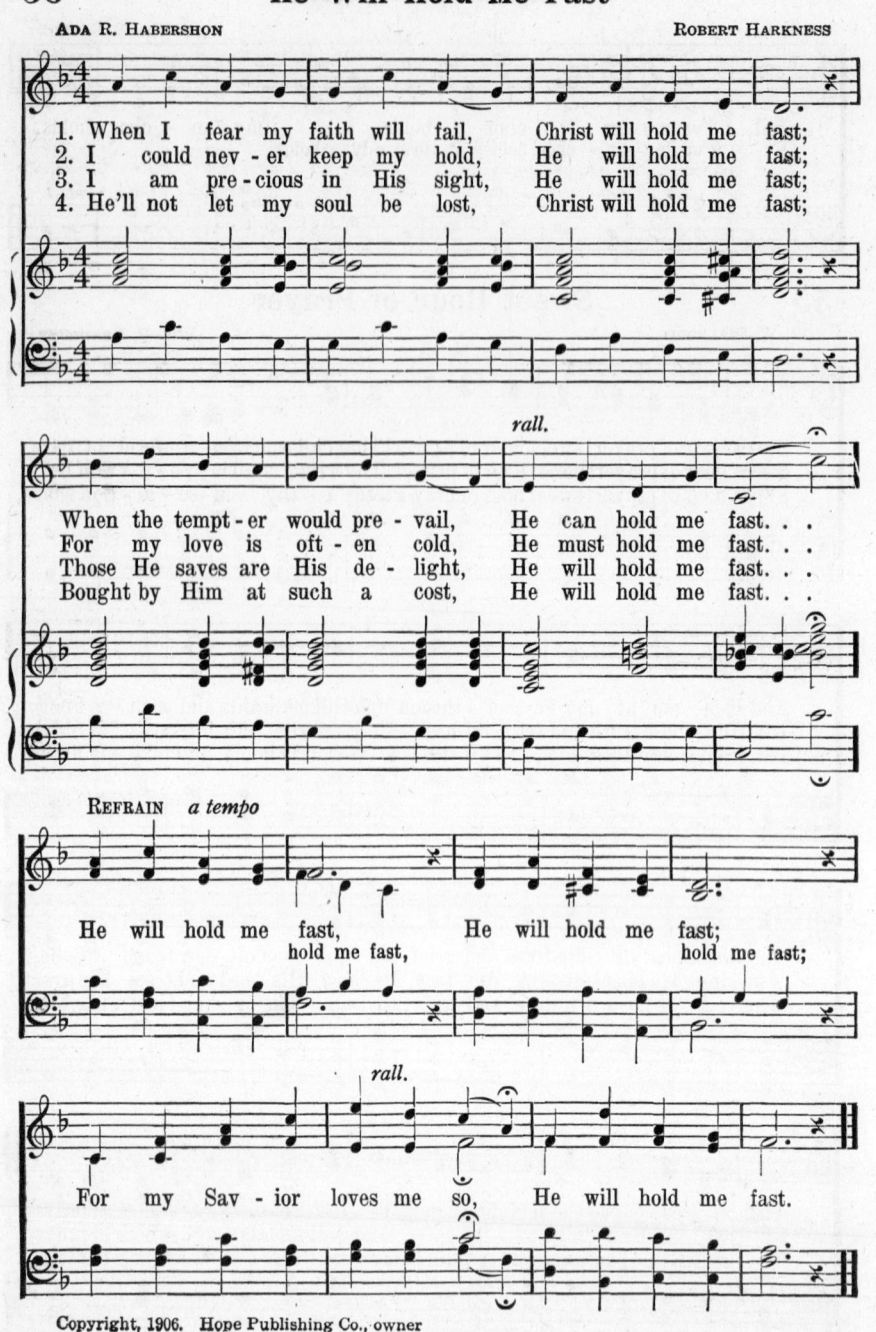

ADA R. HABERSHON  
ROBERT HARKNESS

1. When I fear my faith will fail, Christ will hold me fast;
   When the tempt-er would pre-vail, He can hold me fast...
2. I could nev-er keep my hold, He will hold me fast;
   For my love is oft-en cold, He must hold me fast...
3. I am pre-cious in His sight, He will hold me fast;
   Those He saves are His de-light, He will hold me fast...
4. He'll not let my soul be lost, Christ will hold me fast;
   Bought by Him at such a cost, He will hold me fast...

**Refrain** *a tempo*

He will hold me fast, He will hold me fast;
  hold me fast,        hold me fast;
For my Sav-ior loves me so, He will hold me fast.

Copyright, 1906. Hope Publishing Co., owner

# 57 Under His Wings

WILLIAM O. CUSHING     IRA D. SANKEY

1. Un-der His wings I am safe-ly a-bid-ing; Tho' the night deep-ens and tem-pests are wild, Still I can trust Him; I know He will keep me; He has re-deemed me, and I am His child.
2. Un-der His wings, what a ref-uge in sor-row! How the heart yearn-ing-ly turns to His rest! Oft-en when earth has no balm for my heal-ing, There I find com-fort, and there I am blest.
3. Un-der His wings, O what pre-cious en-joy-ment! There will I hide till life's tri-als are o'er; Shel-tered, pro-tect-ed, no e-vil can harm me; Rest-ing in Je-sus I'm safe ev-er-more.

**CHORUS**

Un-der His wings, un-der His wings, Who from His love can sev-er? Un-der His wings my soul shall a-bide, Safe-ly a-bide for-ev-er.

Copyright, 1924, by G. V. Sankey. Renewal. Hope Publishing Company, owner

## 58. When the Roll is Called Up Yonder

J. M. B.  
J. M. Black

1. When the trumpet of the Lord shall sound, and time shall be no more, And the morning breaks, e-ter-nal, bright and fair; When the saved of earth shall gather o-ver on the oth-er shore, And the roll is called up yon-der, I'll be there.
2. On that bright and cloudless morning when the dead in Christ shall rise, And the glo-ry of His res-ur-rec-tion share; When His cho-sen ones shall gather to their home beyond the skies, And the roll is called up yon-der, I'll be there.
3. Let us la-bor for the Mas-ter from the dawn till set-ting sun, Let us talk of all His wondrous love and care; Then when all of life is o-ver, and our work on earth is done, And the roll is called up yon-der, I'll be there.

**Chorus.**

When the roll . . . . . is called up yon - - - der, When the roll . . . is called up yon - - der, When the roll . . . . is called up
When the roll is called up yon-der, I'll be there, When the roll is called up yon-der, I'll be there, When the roll is called up

Copyright, 1921, Renewal. Hope Publishing Co., owner

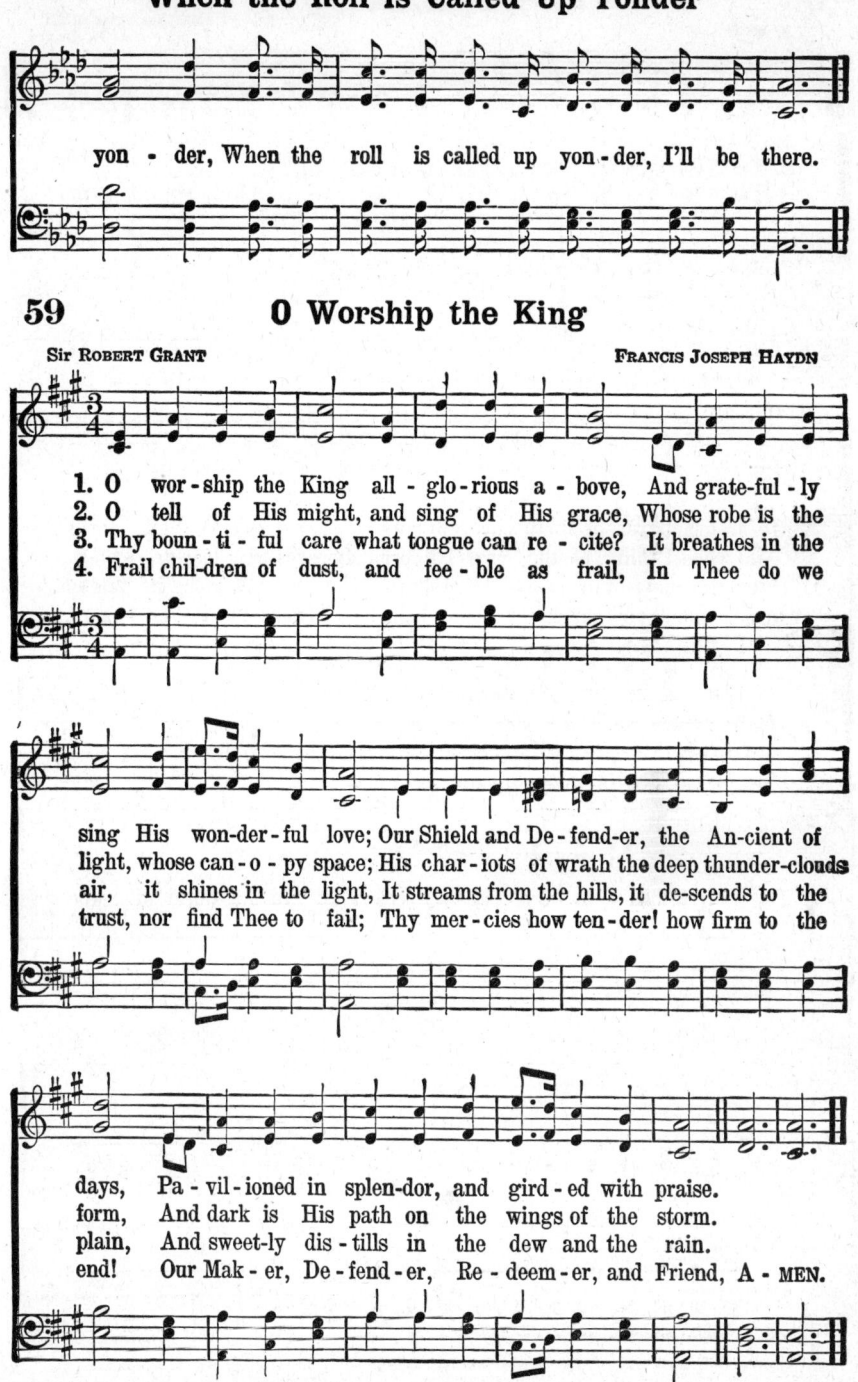

# When the Roll is Called Up Yonder

yon-der, When the roll is called up yon-der, I'll be there.

## 59  O Worship the King

Sir Robert Grant  
Francis Joseph Haydn

1. O wor-ship the King all-glo-rious a-bove, And grate-ful-ly
2. O tell of His might, and sing of His grace, Whose robe is the
3. Thy boun-ti-ful care what tongue can re-cite? It breathes in the
4. Frail chil-dren of dust, and fee-ble as frail, In Thee do we

sing His won-der-ful love; Our Shield and De-fend-er, the An-cient of
light, whose can-o-py space; His char-iots of wrath the deep thunder-clouds
air, it shines in the light, It streams from the hills, it de-scends to the
trust, nor find Thee to fail; Thy mer-cies how ten-der! how firm to the

days, Pa-vil-ioned in splen-dor, and gird-ed with praise.
form, And dark is His path on the wings of the storm.
plain, And sweet-ly dis-tills in the dew and the rain.
end! Our Mak-er, De-fend-er, Re-deem-er, and Friend, A-MEN.

## 60 Ivory Palaces

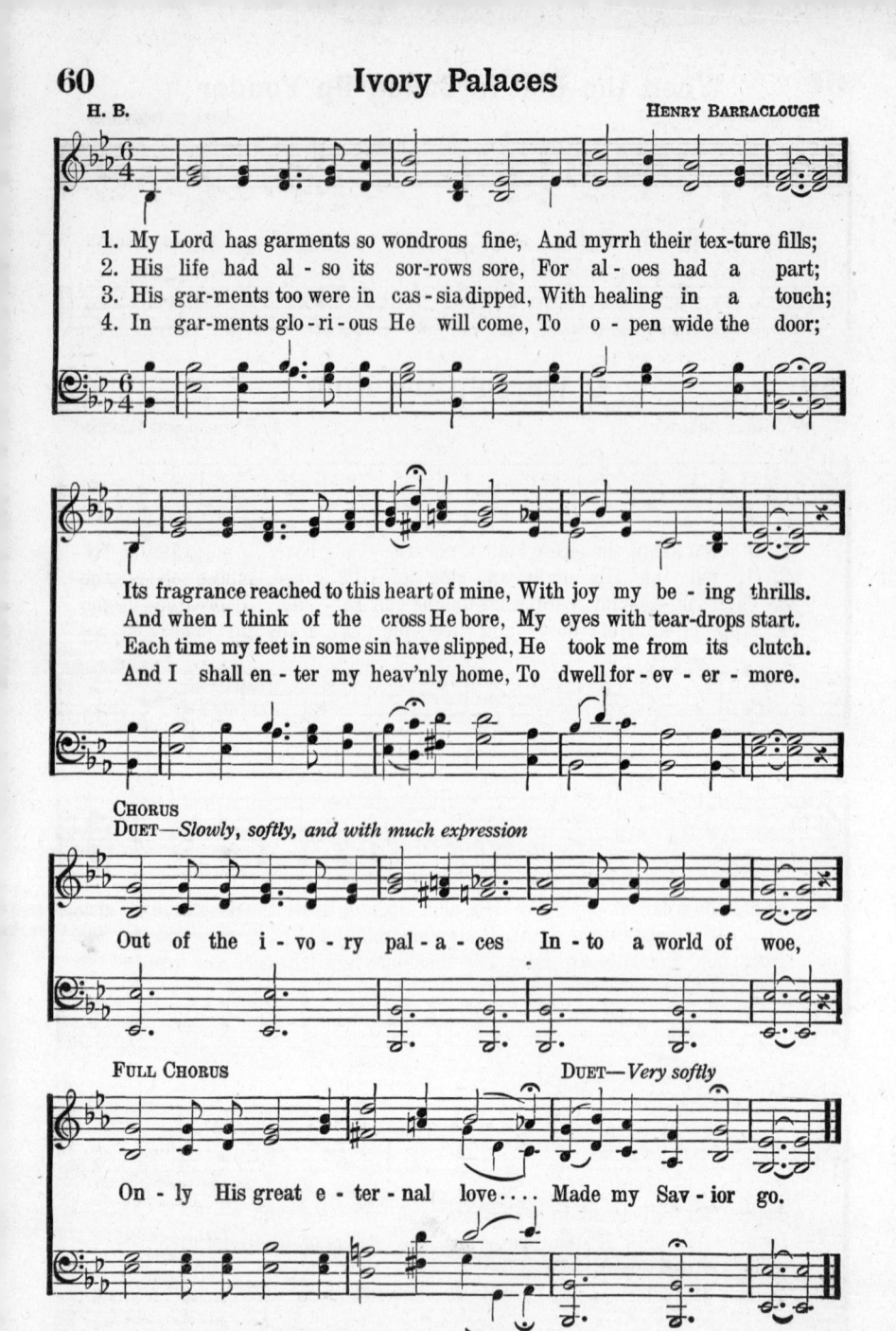

H. B.                                                                                                        Henry Barraclough

1. My Lord has garments so wondrous fine, And myrrh their tex-ture fills;
2. His life had al - so its sor-rows sore, For al - oes had a part;
3. His gar-ments too were in cas - sia dipped, With healing in a touch;
4. In gar-ments glo - ri - ous He will come, To o - pen wide the door;

Its fragrance reached to this heart of mine, With joy my be - ing thrills.
And when I think of the cross He bore, My eyes with tear-drops start.
Each time my feet in some sin have slipped, He took me from its clutch.
And I shall en - ter my heav'nly home, To dwell for - ev - er - more.

**Chorus**
Duet—*Slowly, softly, and with much expression*

Out of the i - vo - ry pal - a - ces In - to a world of woe,

**Full Chorus**                                       Duet—*Very softly*

On - ly His great e - ter - nal love.... Made my Sav - ior go.

Copyright, 1915. Hope Publishing Co., owner

## 61. Saved By Grace

FANNY J. CROSBY  
GEO. C. STEBBINS

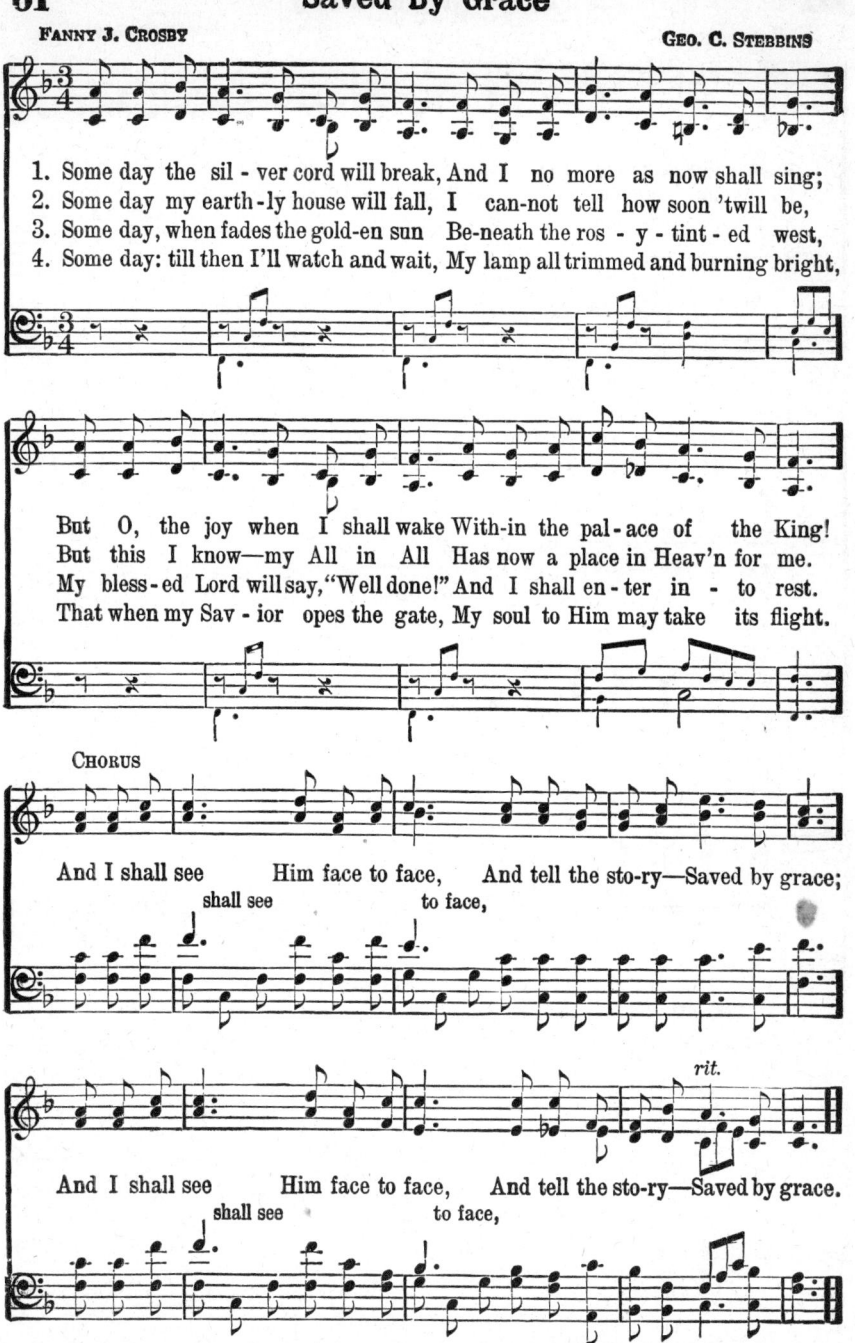

1. Some day the sil-ver cord will break, And I no more as now shall sing;
2. Some day my earth-ly house will fall, I can-not tell how soon 'twill be,
3. Some day, when fades the gold-en sun Be-neath the ros-y-tint-ed west,
4. Some day: till then I'll watch and wait, My lamp all trimmed and burning bright,

But O, the joy when I shall wake With-in the pal-ace of the King!
But this I know—my All in All Has now a place in Heav'n for me.
My bless-ed Lord will say, "Well done!" And I shall en-ter in-to rest.
That when my Sav-ior opes the gate, My soul to Him may take its flight.

**CHORUS**

And I shall see Him face to face, And tell the sto-ry—Saved by grace;
shall see          to face,

And I shall see Him face to face, And tell the sto-ry—Saved by grace.
shall see          to face,

Copyright, 1921, by Geo. C. Stebbins. Renewal. Hope Publishing Company, owner

# Sweet By and By

S. F. Bennett        J. P. Webster

1. There's a land that is fair-er than day, And by faith we can see it a-far; For the Fa-ther waits o-ver the way, To pre-pare us a dwell-ing-place there.
2. We shall sing on that beau-ti-ful shore The mel-o-di-ous songs of the blest, And our spir-its shall sor-row no more, Not a sigh for the bless-ing of rest.
3. To our boun-ti-ful Fa-ther a-bove, We will of-fer our trib-ute of praise, For the glo-ri-ous gift of His love, And the bless-ings that hal-low our days.

**Chorus**

In the sweet by and by, We shall meet on that beau-ti-ful shore; In the sweet by and by, We shall meet on that beau-ti-ful shore.

Copyright, 1910, by Joan H. Webster

## 63. I Choose Jesus

JAMES ROWE  
SAMUEL W. BEAZLEY

1. When I need some-one in time of grief, Some-one my cheer to be,
2. When I need some-one to guide my soul O-ver the storm-y sea,
3. When I need help to de-feat the foe, Some-one my shield to be,
4. When all my tri-als on earth are o'er, And the dark stream I see,

Je-sus I choose, for He gives re-lief, He is the best for me.
Al-ways to Je-sus I give con-trol, He is the best for me.
Al-ways to Je-sus in faith I go, He is the best for me.
Je-sus shall bear me to yon-der shore; He is the best for me.

**Chorus**

I choose Je-sus when I need a friend;.. What I
Yes, I choose my Sav-ior al-ways when I need a help-ful friend; What I need I

need I know that He will send;.. I have proved Him,
know that sure-ly He to me will free-ly send; I have proved Him o'er and o'er, and

good and true is He;.. I choose Je-sus, He is the best for me...
al-ways good and true is He; Yes, I choose my Savior dear, He is the best of all for me.

Copyright, 1913, by Hildebrand-Burnett Co. Robert H. Coleman, owner

## 64. Rescue the Perishing

FANNY J. CROSBY         WILLIAM H. DOANE

1. Res-cue the per-ish-ing, Care for the dy-ing, Snatch them in pit-y from sin and the grave; Weep o'er the er-ring one, Lift up the fall-en,
2. Tho' they are slighting Him, Still He is wait-ing, Wait-ing the pen-i-tent child to re-ceive; Plead with them ear-nest-ly, Plead with them gen-tly,
3. Down in the hu-man heart, Crushed by the tempter, Feel-ings lie bur-ied that grace can re-store; Touched by a lov-ing heart, Wak-ened by kind-ness,
4. Res-cue the per-ish-ing, Du-ty de-mands it; Strength for thy la-bor the Lord will pro-vide; Back to the nar-row way Pa-tient-ly win them;

**CHORUS**

Tell them of Je-sus the migh-ty to save.
He will for-give if they on-ly be-lieve. Res-cue the per-ish-ing,
Chords that are bro-ken will vi-brate once more.
Tell the poor wan-d'rer a Sav-ior has died.

Care for the dy-ing; Je-sus is mer-ci-ful, Je-sus will save.

Copyright property of W. H. Doane

# 65  Throw Out the Life-Line

Edward S. Ufford

E. S. Ufford
Arr. by George C. Stebbins

1. Throw out the Life-Line a-cross the dark wave, There is a broth-er whom
2. Throw out the Life-Line with hand quick and strong: Why do you tar-ry, why
3. Throw out the Life-Line to dan-ger-fraught men, Sink-ing in an-guish where
4. Soon will the sea-son of res-cue be o'er, Soon will they drift to e-

some one should save; Somebody's broth-er! oh, who then, will dare To throw out the
lin-ger so long? See! he is sink-ing; oh; has-ten to-day—And out with the
you've nev-er been: Winds of temp-ta-tion and bil-lows of woe Will soon hurl them
ter-ni-ty's shore, Haste then, my brother, no time for de-lay, But throw out the

**Chorus.**

Life-Line, his per-il to share?
Life-Boat! a-way, then, a-way! Throw out the Life-Line! Throw out the Life-Line!
out where the dark wa-ters flow.
Life-Line and save them to-day.

1. Some one is drift-ing a-way;  2. Some one is sink-ing to-day. A-men.

Used by permission of Biglow & Main Company

# 66. The Fight is On

C. H. M.  
Mrs. C. H. Morris

1. The fight is on, the trumpet sound is ringing out, The cry "To arms!" is heard afar and near; The Lord of hosts is marching on to victory, The triumph of the Christ will soon appear.
2. The fight is on, arouse, ye soldiers brave and true! Jehovah leads, and vict'ry will assure; Go, buckle on the armor God has given you, And in His strength unto the end endure.
3. The Lord is leading on to certain victory; The bow of promise spans the eastern sky; His glorious name in ev'ry land shall honored be; The morn will break, the dawn of peace is nigh.

**Chorus.** *Unison*

The fight is on, O Christian soldier, And face to face in stern array,... With armor gleaming, and colors streaming, The right and wrong engage to-day!

Copyright, 1905, by Wm. J. Kirkpatrick. Hope Publishing Co., owner

## The Fight is On

HARMONY

The fight is on, but be not wea-ry; Be strong, and in His might hold fast; If God be
for us, His ban-ner o'er us, We'll sing the vic-tor's song at last!
Vic-t'ry! Vic-t'ry!

---

### 67  Pass Me Not

FANNY J. CROSBY
W. H. DOANE

1. Pass me not, O gen-tle Sav-ior, Hear my hum-ble cry; While on oth-ers
2. Let me at a throne of mer-cy Find a sweet re-lief; Kneel-ing there in
3. Trust-ing on-ly in Thy mer-it, Would I seek Thy face; Heal my wounded,
4. Thou the Spring of all my com-fort, More than life to me, Whom have I on

Thou art call-ing, Do not pass me by.
deep con-tri-tion, Help my un-be-lief.
bro-ken spir-it, Save me by Thy grace.
earth beside Thee? Whom in Heav'n but Thee?

CHORUS

Sav-ior, Sav-ior, Hear my humble cry; While on oth-ers Thou art call-ing, Do not pass me by.

Copyright property of Fannie T. Doane

# 68    Blessed Assurance

Fanny J. Crosby     Mrs. J. F. Knapp

1. Bless-ed as-sur-ance, Je-sus is mine! Oh, what a fore-taste of glo-ry di-vine! Heir of sal-va-tion, pur-chase of God, Born of His Spir-it, washed in His blood.
2. Per-fect sub-mis-sion, per-fect de-light, Vi-sions of rap-ture now burst on my sight; An-gels de-scend-ing, bring from a-bove Ech-oes of mer-cy, whis-pers of love.
3. Per-fect sub-mis-sion, all is at rest, I in my Sav-ior am hap-py and blest; Watching and wait-ing, look-ing a-bove, Filled with His goodness, lost in His love.

**Chorus**

This is my sto-ry, this is my song, Prais-ing my Sav-ior all the day long; This is my sto-ry, this is my song, Prais-ing my Sav-ior all the day long.

# 69. The Solid Rock

EDWARD MOTE — WILLIAM B. BRADBURY

1. My hope is built on noth-ing less Than Je-sus' blood and right-eous-ness;
2. When darkness veils His love-ly face, I rest on His un-chang-ing grace;
3. His oath, His cov-e-nant, His blood, Sup-port me in the whelm-ing flood;
4. When He shall come with trumpet sound, Oh, may I then in Him be found;

I dare not trust the sweet-est frame, But whol-ly lean on Je-sus' name.
In ev-'ry high and storm-y gale, My an-chor holds with-in the veil.
When all a-round my soul gives way, He then is all my hope and stay.
Dressed in His right-eous-ness a-lone, Fault-less to stand be-fore the throne.

**REFRAIN**

On Christ, the sol-id Rock, I stand; All oth-er ground is sink-ing sand, All oth-er ground is sink-ing sand.

## 70 Jesus Saves

PRISCILLA J. OWENS  
WM. J. KIRKPATRICK

1. We have heard the joy-ful sound: Je-sus saves! Je-sus saves!
2. Waft it on the roll-ing tide; Je-sus saves! Je-sus saves!
3. Sing a-bove the bat-tle strife, Je-sus saves! Je-sus saves!
4. Give the winds a might-y voice, Je-sus saves! Je-sus saves!

Spread the ti-dings all a-round: Je-sus saves! Je-sus saves!
Tell to sin-ners far and wide: Je-sus saves! Je-sus saves!
By His death and end-less life, Je-sus saves! Je-sus saves!
Let the na-tions now re-joice,— Je-sus saves! Je-sus saves!

Bear the news to ev-'ry land, Climb the steeps and cross the waves;
Sing, ye is-lands of the sea; Ech-o back, ye o-cean caves;
Sing it soft-ly thro' the gloom, When the heart for mer-cy craves;
Shout sal-va-tion full and free; High-est hills and deep-est caves;

On-ward!—'tis our Lord's com-mand; Je-sus saves! Je-sus saves!
Earth shall keep her ju-bi-lee: Je-sus saves! Je-sus saves!
Sing in tri-umph o'er the tomb,— Je-sus saves! Je-sus saves!
This our song of vic-to-ry,— Je-sus saves! Je-sus saves!

Copyright, 1910, by Wm. J. Kirkpatrick, in renewal  Hope Publishing Company, owner

# 71. Christ Liveth in Me

EL NATHAN  
JAMES McGRANAHAN

1. Once far from God and dead in sin, No light my heart could see;
2. As rays of light from yon-der sun, The flow'rs of earth set free,
3. As lives the flow'r with-in the seed, As in the cone the tree,
4. With long-ing all my heart is filled, That like Him I may be,

But in God's Word the light I found, Now Christ liv-eth in me.
So life and light and love came forth From Christ liv-ing in me.
So, praise the God of truth and grace, His Spir-it dwell-eth in me.
As on the won-drous tho't I dwell That Christ liv-eth in me.

**CHORUS.**

Christ liv-eth in me, Christ liv-eth in me,
    Christ liv-eth in me,
                                        Christ liv-eth in
Oh! what a sal-va-tion this, That Christ liv-eth in me.
me, Oh!

Copyright, 1919, Renewal. Hope Publishing Co., owner

## 72. I Am Praying for You

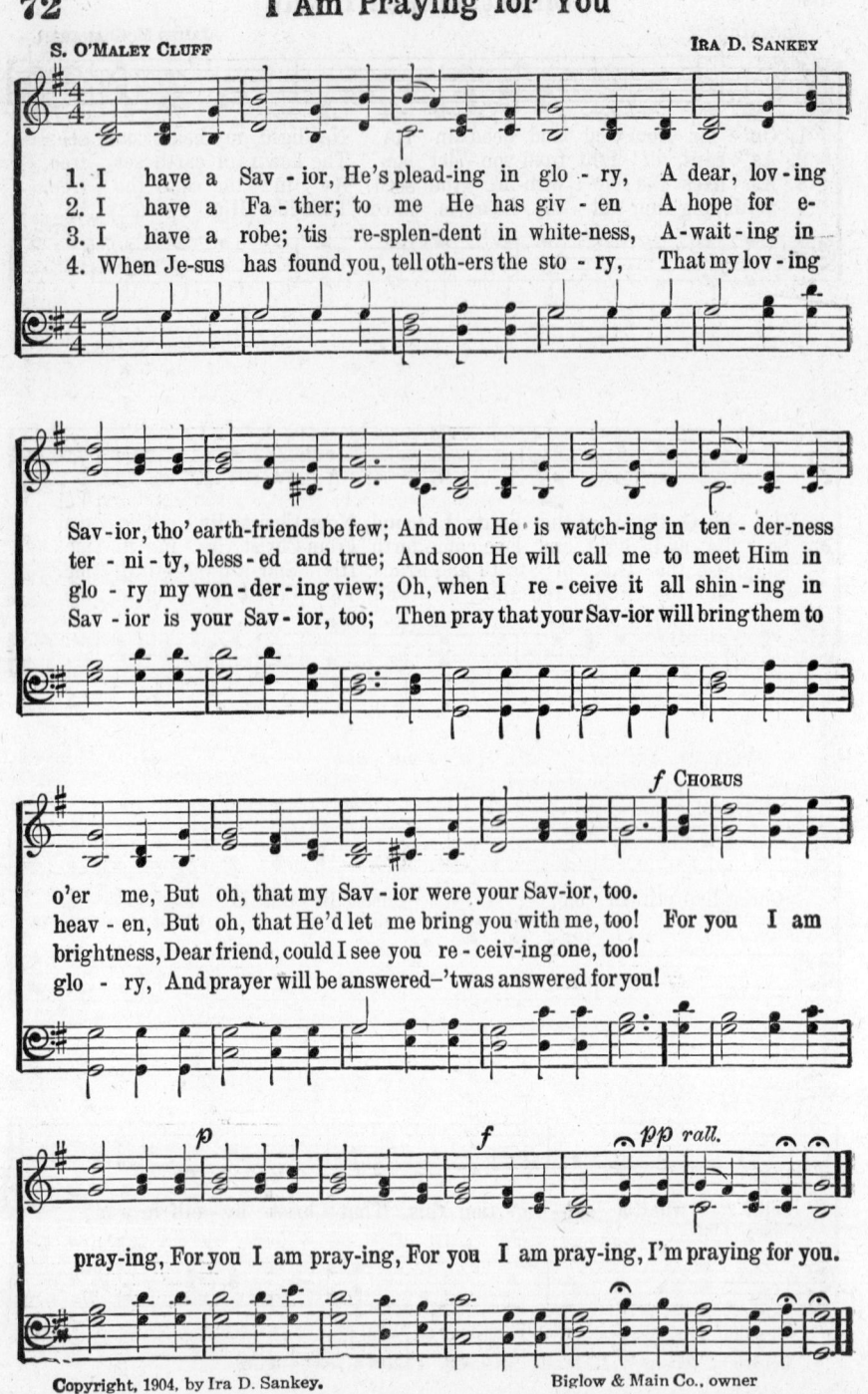

S. O'Maley Cluff  
Ira D. Sankey

1. I have a Sav-ior, He's plead-ing in glo-ry, A dear, lov-ing Sav-ior, tho' earth-friends be few; And now He is watch-ing in ten-der-ness o'er me, But oh, that my Sav-ior were your Sav-ior, too.
2. I have a Fa-ther; to me He has giv-en A hope for e-ter-ni-ty, bless-ed and true; And soon He will call me to meet Him in heav-en, But oh, that He'd let me bring you with me, too!
3. I have a robe; 'tis re-splen-dent in white-ness, A-wait-ing in glo-ry my won-der-ing view; Oh, when I re-ceive it all shin-ing in brightness, Dear friend, could I see you re-ceiv-ing one, too!
4. When Je-sus has found you, tell oth-ers the sto-ry, That my lov-ing Sav-ior is your Sav-ior, too; Then pray that your Sav-ior will bring them to glo-ry, And prayer will be answered—'twas answered for you!

**Chorus**

For you I am pray-ing, For you I am pray-ing, For you I am pray-ing, I'm praying for you.

Copyright, 1904, by Ira D. Sankey.   Biglow & Main Co., owner

# 73. I Am Thine, O Lord

*Fanny J. Crosby* — *W. H. Doane*

1. I am Thine, O Lord, I have heard Thy voice, And it told Thy love to me; But I long to rise in the arms of faith, And be closer drawn to Thee.

2. Con-se-crate me now to Thy serv-ice, Lord, By the pow'r of grace di-vine; Let my soul look up with a stead-fast hope, And my will be lost in Thine.

3. O the pure de-light of a sin-gle hour That be-fore Thy throne I spend, When I kneel in prayer, and with Thee, my God, I com-mune as friend with friend!

4. There are depths of love that I can-not know Till I cross the nar-row sea; There are heights of joy that I may not reach Till I rest in peace with Thee.

**Refrain**

Draw me near-er, near-er, bless-ed Lord, To the cross where Thou hast died; Draw me near-er, near-er, near-er, bless-ed Lord, To Thy pre-cious, bleed-ing side.

Copyright, 1903, by W. H. Doane. Renewal. Fannie T. Doane, owner.

## 74 We're Marching to Zion

ISAAC WATTS
*Spirited*

ROBERT LOWRY

1. Come, we that love the Lord, And let our joys be known, Join in a song with sweet ac-cord, Join in a song with sweet ac-cord, And thus sur-round the throne, And thus sur-round the throne.
2. Let those re-fuse to sing Who nev-er knew our God; But chil-dren of the heav'n-ly King, But chil-dren of the heav'n-ly King, May speak their joys a-broad, May speak their joys a-broad.
3. The hill of Zi-on yields A thou-sand sa-cred sweets Be-fore we reach the heav'n-ly fields, Be-fore we reach the heav'n-ly fields, Or walk the gold-en streets, Or walk the gold-en streets.
4. Then let our songs a-bound, And ev-'ry tear be dry; We're marching thro' Immanuel's ground, We're marching thro' Immanuel's ground, To fair-er worlds on high, To fair-er worlds on high.

**CHORUS**

We're march-ing to Zi-on, Beau-ti-ful, beau-ti-ful Zi-on; We're marching up-ward to Zi-on, The beau-ti-ful cit-y of God.
We're march-ing on to Zi-on, Zi-on, Zi-on, thus sur-round the throne, And thus sur-round the throne.

Copyright, property of Mary Runyon Lowry. Used by permission

# 75  Beulah Land

EDGAR PAGE  
JNO. R. SWENEY

1. I've reached the land of corn and wine, And all its rich-es free-ly mine;
2. My Sav-ior comes and walks with me, And sweet com-mun-ion here have we;
3. A sweet per-fume up-on the breeze Is borne from ev-er-ver-nal trees,
4. The zeph-yrs seem to float to me, Sweet sounds of Heaven's mel-o-dy,

Here shines undimmed one bliss-ful day, For all my night has passed a-way.
He gen-tly leads me by His hand, For this is Heav-en's bor-der-land.
And flow'rs, that nev-er-fad-ing grow, Where streams of life for-ev-er flow.
As an-gels with the white-robed throng Join in the sweet Re-demp-tion song.

CHORUS

O Beu-lah Land, sweet Beu-lah Land, As on thy high-est mount I stand,

I look a-way a-cross the sea, Where man-sions are pre-pared for me, And

view the shin-ing glo-ry-shore,—My Heav'n, my home for-ev-er-more!

Used by permission of Mrs. Jno. R. Sweney

# 76. It is Glory Just to Walk With Him

AVIS M. BURGESON  
HALDOR LILLENAS

1. It is glo-ry just to walk with Him whose blood has ransomed me; It is
2. It is glo-ry when the shad-ows fall, to know that He is near; Oh! what
3. 'Twill be glo-ry when I walk with Him on heav-en's gold-en shore, Nev-er

rap-ture for my soul each day; It is joy di-vine to feel Him near wher-e'er my
joy to sim-ply trust and pray! It is glo-ry to a-bide in Him when skies a-
from His side a-gain to stray; 'Twill be glo-ry, wondrous glo-ry with the Sav-ior

**CHORUS**

path may be; Bless the Lord, it's glo-ry all the way!
bove are clear; Yes, with Him, it's glo-ry all the way!   It is glo-ry just to walk with
ev - er-more, Ev - er - last-ing glo-ry all the way!

Him,...... It is glo-ry just to walk with Him;..... He will guide my steps aright,
walk with Him,                                walk with Him;

Thro' the vale and o'er the height; It is glo-ry just to walk with Him......
                                                                    walk with Him.

Copyright, 1918. Hope Publishing Co., owner

## 77 We've a Story to Tell

Colin Sterne
Voices in Unison

H. E. Nichol

1. We've a sto-ry to tell to the na-tions, That shall turn their hearts to the right; A sto-ry of truth and sweet-ness, A sto-ry of peace and light,... A sto-ry of peace and light.
2. We've a song to be sung to the na-tions, That shall lift their hearts to the Lord; A song that shall con-quer e-vil And shat-ter the spear and sword,. And shat-ter the spear and sword.
3. We've a mes-sage to give to the na-tions, That the Lord who reign-eth a-bove, Hath sent us His Son to save us, And show us that God is love,.. And show us that God is love.
4. We've a Sav-ior to show to the na-tions, Who the path of sor-row has trod, That all of the world's great peo-ple Might come to the truth of God,.. Might come to the truth of God!

Refrain

For the darkness shall turn to dawn-ing, And the dawn-ing to noon-day bright,
And Christ's great kingdom shall come on earth, The kingdom of love and light.

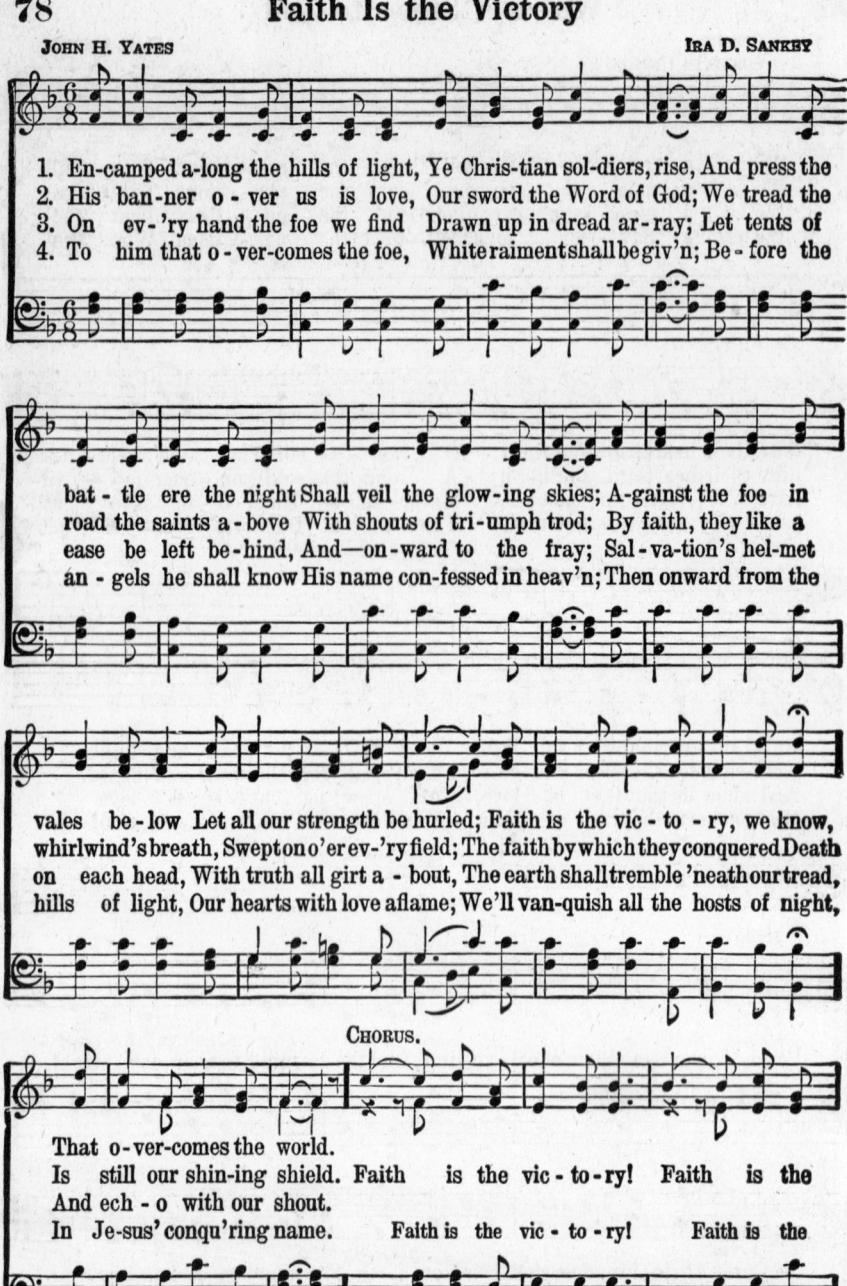

## 78. Faith Is the Victory

JOHN H. YATES  
IRA D. SANKEY

1. En-camped a-long the hills of light, Ye Chris-tian sol-diers, rise, And press the bat-tle ere the night Shall veil the glow-ing skies; A-gainst the foe in vales be-low Let all our strength be hurled; Faith is the vic-to-ry, we know, That o-ver-comes the world.

2. His ban-ner o-ver us is love, Our sword the Word of God; We tread the road the saints a-bove With shouts of tri-umph trod; By faith, they like a whirlwind's breath, Swept on o'er ev-'ry field; The faith by which they conquered Death Is still our shin-ing shield.

3. On ev-'ry hand the foe we find Drawn up in dread ar-ray; Let tents of ease be left be-hind, And—on-ward to the fray; Sal-va-tion's hel-met on each head, With truth all girt a-bout, The earth shall tremble 'neath our tread, And ech-o with our shout.

4. To him that o-ver-comes the foe, White raiment shall be giv'n; Be-fore the an-gels he shall know His name con-fessed in heav'n; Then onward from the hills of light, Our hearts with love aflame; We'll van-quish all the hosts of night, In Je-sus' conqu'ring name.

CHORUS.

Faith is the vic-to-ry! Faith is the vic-to-ry! Faith is the

Copyright, 1919, by G. V. Sankey. Renewal. Hope Publishing Company. owner

## Faith Is the Victory

vic-to-ry! Oh, glo-ri-ous vic-to-ry, That o-ver-comes the world.
vic-to-ry!

## 79 At Calvary

WM. R. NEWELL — D. B. TOWNER

1. Years I spent in van-i-ty and pride, Car-ing not my Lord was cru-ci-fied, Know-ing not it was for me He died On Cal-va-ry.
2. By God's Word at last my sin I learned; Then I trem-bled at the law I'd spurned, Till my guilt-y soul im-plor-ing turned To Cal-va-ry.
3. Now I've giv'n to Je-sus ev-'ry-thing, Now I glad-ly own Him as my King, Now my rap-tured soul can on-ly sing Of Cal-va-ry.
4. O the love that drew sal-va-tion's plan! O the grace that bro't it down to man! O the might-y gulf that God did span At Cal-va-ry!

CHORUS

Mer-cy there was great, and grace was free; Par-don there was mul-ti-plied to me; There my burdened soul found lib-er-ty, At Cal-va-ry.

Copyright. 1923, Renewal. Hope Publishing Co., owner

## 80. Ye Must Be Born Again

W. T. Sleeper

Geo. C. Stebbins

1. A ru-ler once came to Je-sus by night, To ask Him the way of sal-vation and light; The Mas-ter made an-swer in words true and plain,
2. Ye children of men, at-tend to the word So sol-emn-ly ut-tered by Je-sus the Lord; And let not this mes-sage to you be in vain,
3. Oh, ye who would en-ter that glo-ri-ous rest, And sing with the ransomed the song of the blest; The life ev-er-last-ing if ye would ob-tain,
4. A dear one in heaven thy heart yearns to see, At the beautiful gate may be watching for thee; Then list to the note of this sol-emn re-frain,

CHORUS

"Ye must be born a-gain." . . "Ye must be born a-gain, . . Ye must be born a-gain; . . I ver-i-ly, ver-i-ly say un-to thee, Ye must be born a-gain." . . .

Copyright, 1918. Renewal. Hope Publishing Co., owner

## 81. I Love to Tell the Story

CATHERINE HANKEY  
WILLIAM G. FISCHER

1. I love to tell the sto-ry Of un-seen things a-bove, Of Je-sus and His glo-ry, Of Je-sus and His love. I love to tell the sto-ry, Be-cause I know 'tis true; It sat-is-fies my longings As noth-ing else can do.

2. I love to tell the sto-ry, More won-der-ful it seems Than all the gold-en fan-cies Of all our gold-en dreams. I love to tell the sto-ry, It did so much for me; And that is just the rea-son I tell it now to thee.

3. I love to tell the sto-ry, 'Tis pleas-ant to re-peat What seems, each time I tell it, More won-der-ful-ly sweet. I love to tell the sto-ry, For some have nev-er heard The mes-sage of sal-va-tion From God's own ho-ly word.

4. I love to tell the sto-ry, For those who know it best Seem hun-ger-ing and thirst-ing To hear it like the rest. And when, in scenes of glo-ry, I sing the new, new song, 'Twill be the old, old sto-ry That I have loved so long.

CHORUS

I love to tell the sto-ry, 'Twill be my theme in glo-ry To tell the old, old sto-ry Of Jesus and His love.

Used by permission of W. G. Fischer.

## 82 Higher Ground

JOHNSON OATMAN, JR.  CHAS. H. GABRIEL

1. I'm press-ing on the up-ward way, New heights I'm gaining ev-'ry day;
2. My heart has no de-sire to stay Where doubts a-rise and fears dis-may;
3. I want to live a-bove the world, Tho' Sa-tan's darts at me are hurled;
4. I want to scale the utmost height, And catch a gleam of glo-ry bright;

Still pray-ing as I on-ward bound, "Lord, plant my feet on high-er ground."
Tho' some may dwell where these abound, My prayer, my aim, is high-er ground.
For faith has caught the joy-ful sound, The song of saints on high-er ground.
But still I'll pray till Heav'n I've found, "Lord, lead me on to high-er ground."

CHORUS

Lord, lift me up and let me stand, By faith, on Heav-en's ta-ble-land,

A high-er plane than I have found; Lord, plant my feet on high-er ground.

Copyright, 1898, by J. Howard Entwisle. John J. Hood, owner

# 83  He Hideth My Soul

FANNY J. CROSBY  
WM. J. KIRKPATRICK  
*Allegretto*

1. A won-der-ful Sav-ior is Je-sus my Lord, A won-der-ful Sav-ior to me, He hid-eth my soul in the cleft of the rock, Where riv-ers of pleas-ure I see.
2. A won-der-ful Sav-ior is Je-sus my Lord, He tak-eth my bur-den a-way, He hold-eth me up, and I shall not be moved, He giv-eth me strength as my day.
3. With num-ber-less bless-ings each mo-ment He crowns, And filled with His full-ness di-vine, I sing in my rap-ture, oh, glo-ry to God For such a Re-deem-er as mine!
4. When clothed in His brightness, transport-ed I rise To meet Him in clouds of the sky, His per-fect sal-va-tion, His won-der-ful love, I'll shout with the mil-lions on high.

**CHORUS**

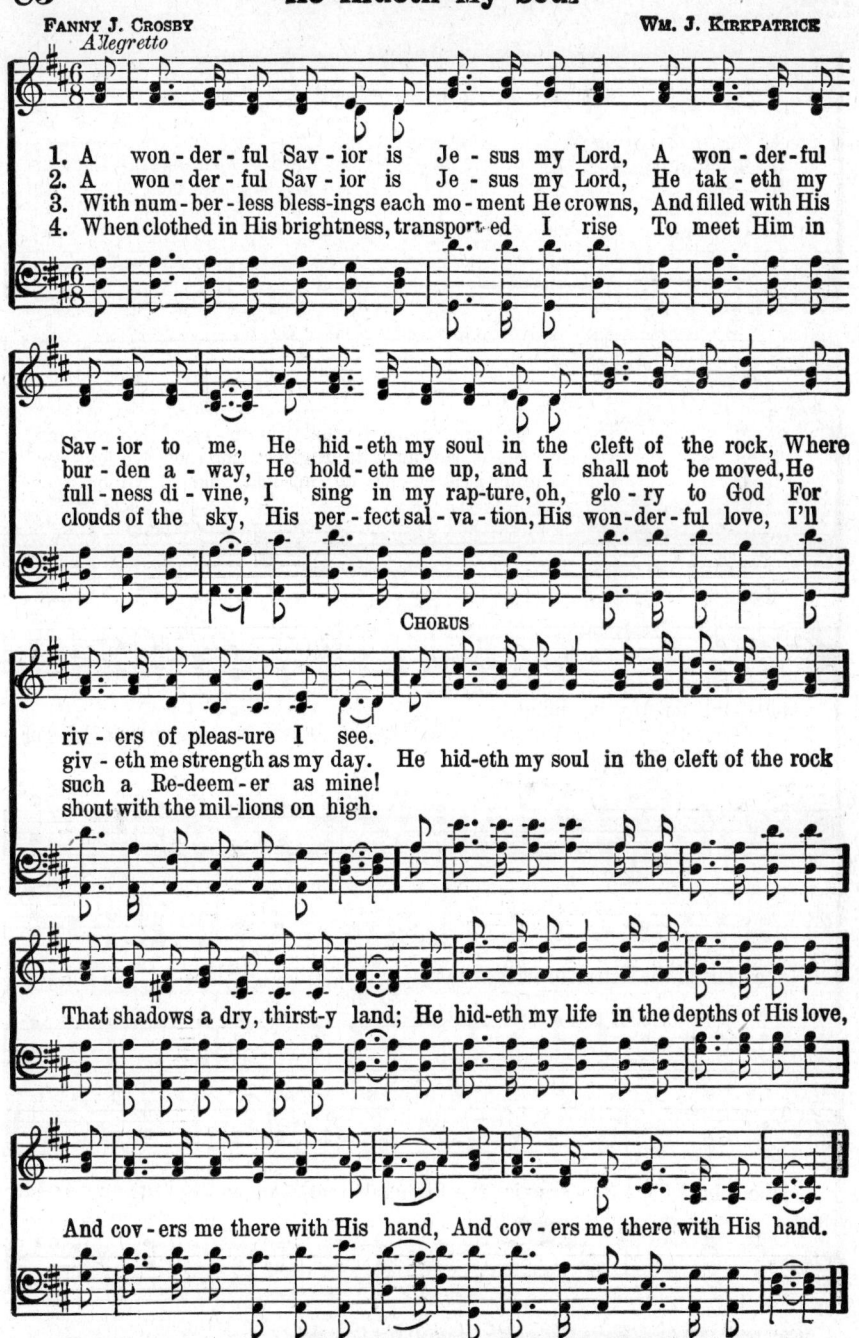

He hid-eth my soul in the cleft of the rock That shadows a dry, thirst-y land; He hid-eth my life in the depths of His love, And cov-ers me there with His hand, And cov-ers me there with His hand.

Copyright, 1918, by Wm. J. Kirkpatrick. Renewal. Hope Publishing Co., Owner

## 84  No Longer Lonely

R. H.  
Robert Harkness

1. On life's pathway I am nev-er lone-ly, My Lord is with me, my Lord di-vine;   Ev-er pre-sent Guide, I trust Him on-ly, No lon-ger lone-ly, for He is mine.
2. I shall not be lone-ly in my sor-row, He will sus-tain me un-til the end;   Dark-est night He turns to brightest mor-row, No lon-ger lone-ly! He is my Friend.
3. I shall not be lone-ly in the val-ley, Tho' shadows gath-er, I will not fear;   He has prom-ised ev-er to up-hold me, No lon-ger lone-ly! He will be near.

CHORUS

No longer lone-ly, No longer lone-ly, For Je-sus is the Friend of friends to me; . . . No lon-ger lone-ly, No lon-ger lone-ly, For Je-sus is the Friend of friends to me.

Copyright, 1920, by Robert Harkness. International Copyright secured  
Owned by Robert H. Coleman

## 85. Whosoever, Meaneth Me

J. E. M.  
J. Edwin McConnell

1. I am happy to-day and the sun shines bright, The clouds have been rolled away; For the Savior said, Whosoever will May come with Him to stay. (to stay.)
2. All my hopes have been raised, O His name be praised, His glory has filled my soul; I've been lifted up, and from sin set free, His blood has made me whole. (me whole.)
3. O what wonderful love, O what grace divine, That Jesus should die for me; I was lost in sin, for the world I pined, But now I am set free. (set free.)

**Chorus**

Whosoever, surely meaneth me, Surely meaneth me, O, surely meaneth me; Whosoever, surely meaneth me, Whosoever, meaneth me.

Copyright, 1914, by Charlie Tillman

# 86 Trust and Obey

J. H. Sammis  
D. B. Towner

1. When we walk with the Lord In the Light of His Word What a glo-ry He sheds on our way! While we do His good-will, He a-bides with us still,
2. Not a shad-ow can rise, Not a cloud in the skies, But His smile quickly drives it a-way; Not a doubt or a fear, Not a sigh nor a tear,
3. Not a bur-den we bear, Not a sor-row we share, But our toil He doth rich-ly re-pay; Not a grief nor a loss, Not a frown or a cross,
4. But we nev-er can prove The de-lights of His love Un-til all on the al-tar we lay; For the fa-vor He shows, And the joy He be-stows,
5. Then in fel-low-ship sweet We will sit at His feet, Or we'll walk by His side in the way; What He says we will do, Where He sends we will go,—

CHORUS.

And with all who will trust and o - bey.
Can a-bide while we trust and o - bey.
But is blest if we trust and o - bey. Trust and o - bey, for there's no oth-er
Are for them who will trust and o - bey.
Nev-er fear, on - ly trust and o - bey.

way To be hap-py in Je-sus, But to trust and o - bey. A-MEN.

Copyright, 1921, Renewal. Hope Publishing Co., owner

## 87. Only a Sinner

JAMES M. GRAY  
D. B. TOWNER

1. Naught have I got-ten but what I re-ceived; Grace hath bestowed it since I have be-lieved; Boast-ing ex-clud-ed, pride I a-base; I'm on-ly a
2. Once I was fool-ish, and sin ruled my heart, Caus-ing my foot-steps from God to de-part; Je-sus hath found me, hap-py my case; I now am a
3. Tears un-a-vail-ing, no mer-it had I; Mer-cy had saved me, or else I must die; Sin had a-larmed me, fearing God's face; But now I'm a
4. Suf-fer a sin-ner whose heart o-ver-flows, Lov-ing his Sav-ior to tell what he knows; Once more to tell it, would I embrace—I'm on-ly a

**CHORUS**

sin-ner saved by grace! On-ly a sin-ner saved by grace! On-ly a sin-ner saved by grace! This is my sto-ry, to God be the glo-ry,—I'm on-ly a sin-ner saved by grace!

Copyright, 1905. Hope Publishing Co., owner

## 88. Since the Fullness of His Love Came In

E. E. Hewitt
B. D. Ackley

1. Once my way was dark and drear-y, For my heart was full of sin,
But the sky is bright and cheer-y, Since the full-ness of His love came in.
2. There is grace for all the low-ly, Grace to keep the trust-ing soul:
Pow'r to cleanse and make me ho-ly, Je - sus shall my yield-ed life con-trol.
3. Let me spread a-broad the sto-ry, Oth-er souls to Je-sus win;
For the cross is now my glo-ry, Since the full-ness of His love came in.

CHORUS

I can nev-er tell how much I love Him, I can nev-er tell His love for me;
For it pass-eth hu-man measure, Like a deep, unfathomed sea;
deep, unfathomed sea;
'Tis re-deeming love in Christ my Sav-ior, In my soul the heav'nly joys be-gin;

Copyright, 1916. Hope Publishing Co., owner

# Since the Fullness of His Love Came In

And I live for Jesus only, Since the fullness of His love came in.

## 89  'Tis So Sweet to Trust in Jesus

LOUISA M. R. STEAD  WM. J. KIRKPATRICK

1. 'Tis so sweet to trust in Jesus, Just to take Him at His Word;
2. O how sweet to trust in Jesus, Just to trust His cleansing blood;
3. Yes, 'tis sweet to trust in Jesus, Just from sin and self to cease;
4. I'm so glad I learned to trust Thee, Precious Jesus, Savior, Friend;

Just to rest upon His promise; Just to know, "Thus saith the Lord."
Just in simple faith to plunge me 'Neath the healing, cleansing flood!
Just from Jesus simply taking Life and rest, and joy and peace.
And I know that Thou art with me, Wilt be with me to the end.

CHORUS

Jesus, Jesus, how I trust Him! How I've proved Him o'er and o'er!

Jesus, Jesus, precious Jesus! O for grace to trust Him more!

Copyright, 1882 and 1910, by Wm. J. Kirkpatrick. Hope Publishing Co., owner

# 90. Is My Name Written There?

M. A. K.  
Frank M. Davis.

1. Lord! I care not for rich-es, Nei-ther sil-ver nor gold; I would make sure of Heav-en, I would en-ter the fold; In the book of Thy king-dom, With its pa-ges so fair, Tell me, Je-sus, my Sav-ior, Is my name writ-ten there?

2. Lord, my sins they are man-y, Like the sands of the sea, But Thy blood, O my Sav-ior, Is suf-fi-cient for me; For Thy prom-ise is writ-ten, In bright letters that glow, "Tho' your sins be as scar-let, I will make them like snow." Is my name writ-ten there?

3. Oh! that beau-ti-ful cit-y, With its man-sions of light, With its glo-ri-fied be-ings, In pure gar-ments of white; Where no e-vil thing com-eth To de-spoil what is fair; Where the an-gels are watching, Is my name writ-ten there?

**Refrain.**

Is my name writ-ten there, On the page white and fair? In the book of Thy king-dom, Is my name writ-ten there? A-MEN.

## 91. O That Will Be Glory

C. H. G.                           Chas. H. Gabriel

1. When all my la-bors and tri-als are o'er, And I am safe on that beau-ti-ful shore, Just to be near the dear Lord I a-dore, Will thro' the a-ges be glo-ry for me.

2. When, by the gift of His in-fi-nite grace, I am ac-cord-ed in Heav-en a place, Just to be there and to look on His face, Will thro' the a-ges be glo-ry for me.

3. Friends will be there I have loved long a-go; Joy like a riv-er a-round me will flow; Yet, just a smile from my Sav-ior, I know, Will thro' the a-ges be glo-ry for me.

**Chorus.** *Faster.*

O that will be glo-ry for me, Glo-ry for me, glo-ry for me; When by His grace I shall look on His face, That will be glo-ry, be glo-ry for me. A-men.

Copyright, 1900, by E. O. Excell. Words and Music.

## 92. Jesus Loves Even Me

P. P. B.  
P. P. Bliss

1. I am so glad that our Father in heav'n Tells of His love in the Book He has giv'n, Wonderful things in the Bible I see; This is the dearest, that Jesus loves me.
2. Tho' I forget Him and wander away, Still He doth love me wherever I stray; Back to His dear loving arms would I flee, When I remember that Jesus loves me.
3. Oh, if there's only one song I can sing, When in His beauty I see the great King, This shall my song in eternity be: "Oh, what a wonder that Jesus loves me."

**Chorus**

I am so glad that Jesus loves me, Jesus loves me, Jesus loves me,
I am so glad that Jesus loves me, Jesus loves even me.

Copyright, 1902, by The John Church Co. Used by permission

## He Lifted Me

Charlotte G. Homer  
Chas. H. Gabriel

1. In lov-ing-kind-ness Je-sus came My soul in mer-cy to re-claim, And from the depths of sin and shame Thro' grace He lift-ed me.
2. He called me long be-fore I heard, Be-fore my sin-ful heart was stirred, But when I took Him at His word, For-giv'n He lift-ed me.
3. His brow was pierced with many a thorn, His hands by cru-el nails were torn, When from my guilt and grief, forlorn, In love He lift-ed me.
4. Now on a high-er plane I dwell, And with my soul I know 'tis well; Yet how or why, I can-not tell, He should have lift-ed me.

**CHORUS.**

From sink-ing sand He lift-ed me, With ten-der hand He lift-ed me, From shades of night to plains of light, O praise His name, He lifted me! A-MEN.

Copyright, 1905. Hope Publishing Co., owner

## 94. Wonderful Things to Know

H. H. L.  
H. H. Lemmel

Voices in Unison
*Simply, and not too fast*

1. 'Tis won-der-ful to know that Je-sus Was once a child like me, And lived on earth and worked and played In His home in Gal-i-lee.
2. More won-der-ful it is to know That He has gone a-bove, To pre-pare a place where I may live For-ev-er in His love.

REFRAIN

Won-der-ful, won-der-ful Je-sus! Who was once a child like me; Won-der-ful, won-der-ful Je-sus! Like Him I want to be.

Copyright, 1921, by H. H. Lemmel

## 95. Into My Heart

(MY PRAYER)

H. D. C.     HARRY D. CLARKE

*Sing prayerfully*

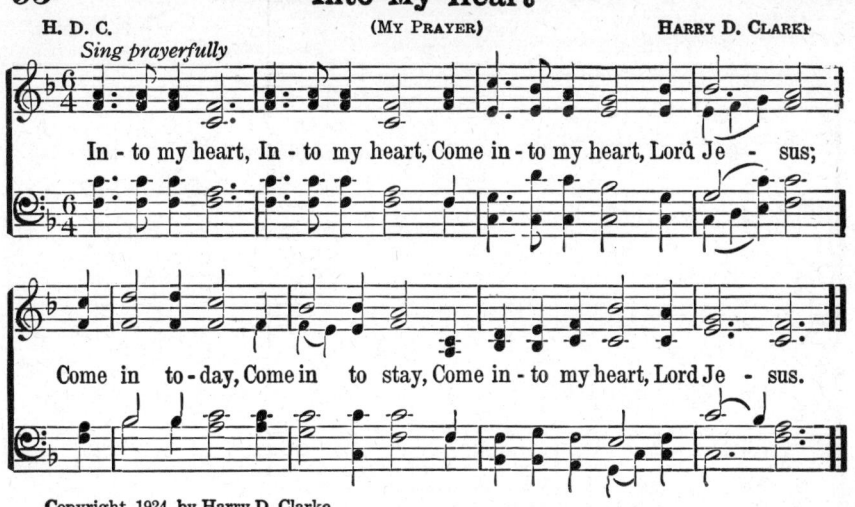

In-to my heart, In-to my heart, Come in-to my heart, Lord Je-sus;
Come in to-day, Come in to stay, Come in-to my heart, Lord Je-sus.

Copyright, 1924, by Harry D. Clarke.

## 96. Dare to Be a Daniel

P. P. B.     P. P. BLISS

1. Stand-ing by a pur-pose true, Heed-ing God's command, Hon-or them, the faith-ful few! All hail to Dan-iel's Band!
2. Man-y might-y men are lost, Dar-ing not to stand, Who for God had been a host, By join-ing Dan-iel's Band!
3. Man-y gi-ants, great and tall, Stalk-ing thro' the land, Headlong to the earth would fall, If met by Dan-iel's Band!
4. Hold the gos-pel ban-ner high! On to vic-t'ry grand! Sa-tan and His host de-fy, And shout for Dan-iel's Band!

CHORUS

Dare to be a Dan-iel, Dare to stand a-lone, Dare to have a pur-pose firm! Dare to make it known!

## 97. God Has Blotted Them Out

ANON.          ANON.

God has blot-ted them out, I'm hap-py and glad and free; God has blot-ted them out, I'll turn to I-sa-iah and see: Chap-ter for-ty-four, Twen-ty-two and three; He's blotted them out and now I can shout, For that means me.

## 98. Everybody Ought to Love Jesus

HARRY DIXON LOES

Ev-'ry-bod-y ought to love Je-sus, Je-sus, Je-sus; He Je-sus Christ, the won-der-ful Sav-ior; died on the cross to save us from sin, Ev-'ry-bod-y ought to love Je-sus.

Copyright, 1917, by H. D. Loes. W. Elmer Bailey, owner. Used by permission

## 99  Do You Wonder Why?

I. A. K.  
IDA A. KORITZ

Do you won-der why it is I *love Him, I *love Him, I *love Him?

Do you won-der why it is I *love Him? I will glad-ly tell you why.

D. S.—*This is why I can-not help but *love Him, Je-sus Christ, who died for me.*

CHORUS

It's be-cause He left His home in glo-ry To die for me.

*Note. Additional verses: trust, serve, and praise Him
Copyright, 1925, by Geo. S. Schuler

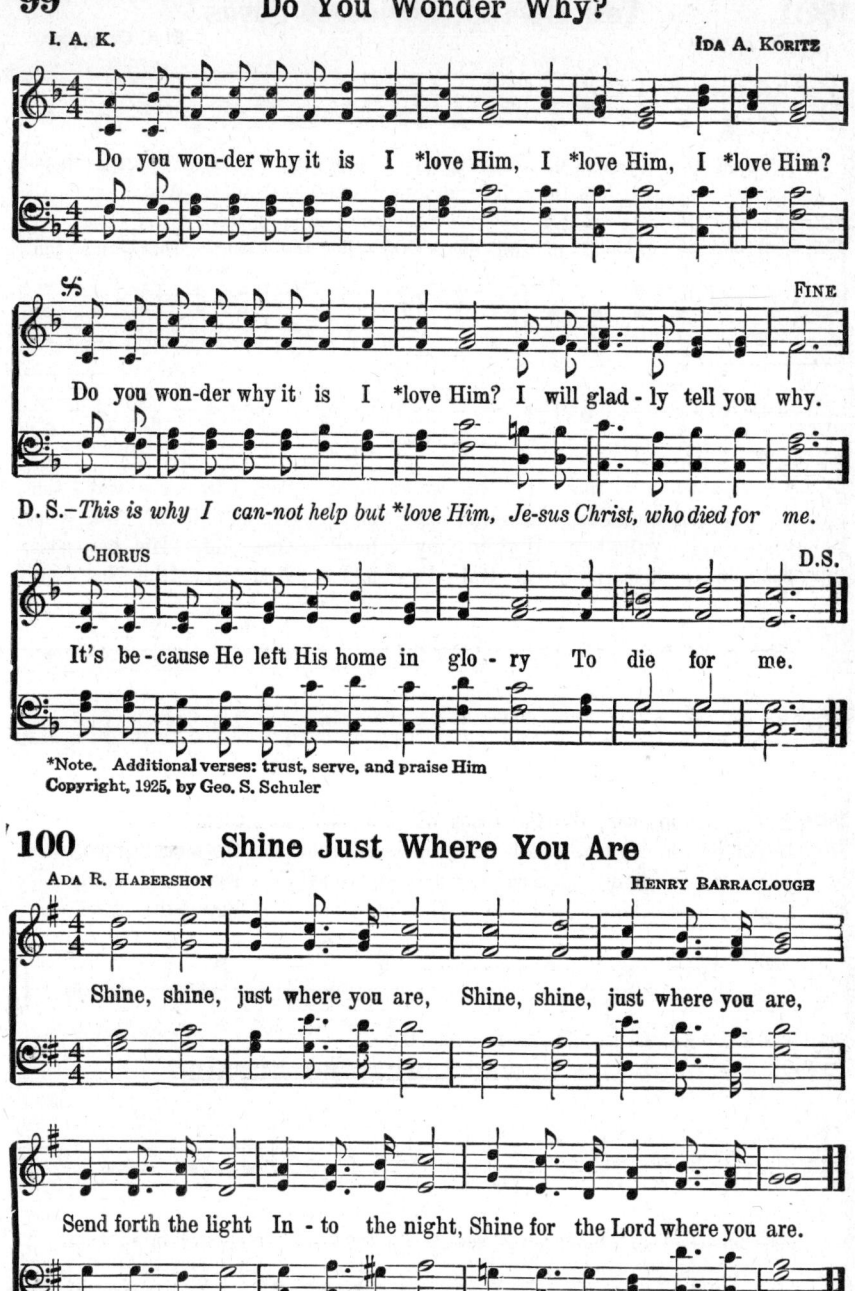

## 100  Shine Just Where You Are

ADA R. HABERSHON  
HENRY BARRACLOUGH

Shine, shine, just where you are, Shine, shine, just where you are,

Send forth the light In-to the night, Shine for the Lord where you are.

Copyright, 1914. Hope Publishing Co., owner

## 101 Tell Me the Stories of Jesus

W. H. Parker  
F. A. Challinor

1. Tell me the sto-ries of Je-sus I love to hear; Things I would ask Him to tell me If He were here; Scenes by the way-side, Tales of the sea, Sto-ries of Je-sus, Tell them to me.
2. First let me hear how the chil-dren Stood round His knee; And I shall fan-cy His bless-ing Rest-ing on me: Words full of kind-ness, Deeds full of grace, All in the love-light Of Je-sus' face.
3. In-to the cit-y I'd fol-low The chil-dren's band, Wav-ing a branch of the palm-tree High in my hand; One of His her-alds, Yes, I would sing Loud-est ho-san-nas! Je-sus is King!
4. Tell me, in ac-cents of won-der, How rolled the sea, Toss-ing the boat in a tem-pest On Gal-i-lee! And how the Mas-ter, Read-y and kind, Chid-ed the bil-lows, And hushed the wind.

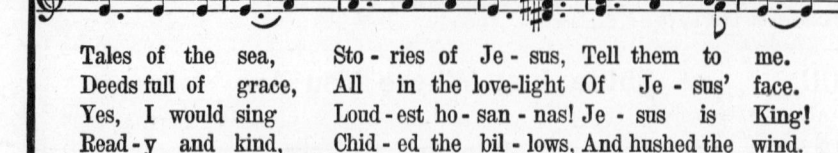

Copyright. By permission of the Sunday-School Union

## 102 Let the Lower Lights Be Burning

P. P. B.  
P. P. Bliss

1. Bright-ly beams our Fa-ther's mer-cy From His light-house ev-er-more,
2. Dark the night of sin has set-tled, Loud the an-gry bil-lows roar;
3. Trim your fee-ble lamp, my broth-er: Some poor sail-or tem-pest tossed,

## Let the Lower Lights Be Burning

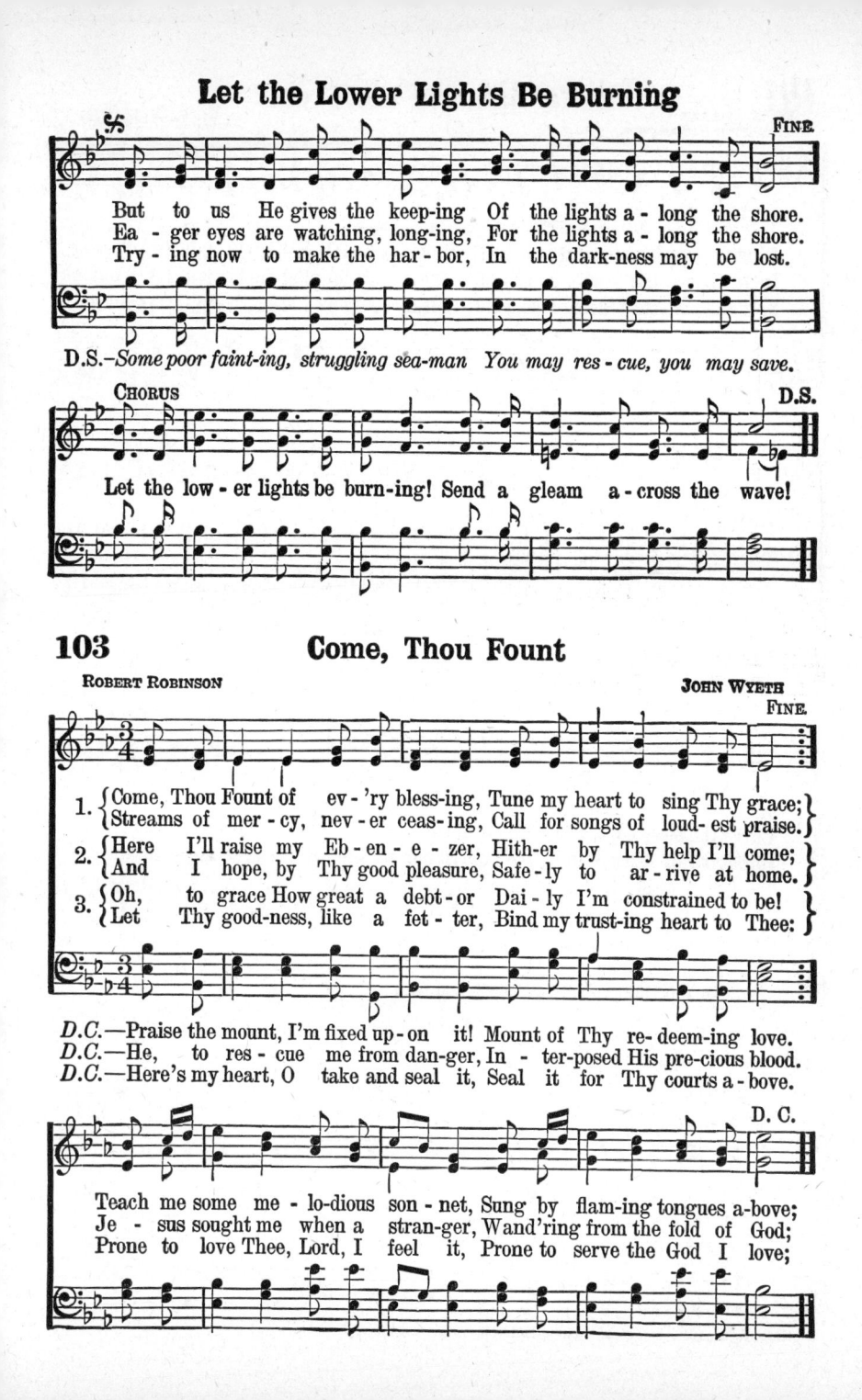

But to us He gives the keep-ing Of the lights a-long the shore.
Ea-ger eyes are watching, long-ing, For the lights a-long the shore.
Try-ing now to make the har-bor, In the dark-ness may be lost.

D.S.—Some poor faint-ing, struggling sea-man You may res-cue, you may save.

**Chorus**

Let the low-er lights be burn-ing! Send a gleam a-cross the wave!

## 103  Come, Thou Fount

ROBERT ROBINSON                          JOHN WYETH

1. {Come, Thou Fount of ev-'ry bless-ing, Tune my heart to sing Thy grace;
   {Streams of mer-cy, nev-er ceas-ing, Call for songs of loud-est praise.
2. {Here I'll raise my Eb-en-e-zer, Hith-er by Thy help I'll come;
   {And I hope, by Thy good pleasure, Safe-ly to ar-rive at home.
3. {Oh, to grace How great a debt-or Dai-ly I'm constrained to be!
   {Let Thy good-ness, like a fet-ter, Bind my trust-ing heart to Thee:

D.C.—Praise the mount, I'm fixed up-on it! Mount of Thy re-deem-ing love.
D.C.—He, to res-cue me from dan-ger, In-ter-posed His pre-cious blood.
D.C.—Here's my heart, O take and seal it, Seal it for Thy courts a-bove.

Teach me some me-lo-dious son-net, Sung by flam-ing tongues a-bove;
Je-sus sought me when a stran-ger, Wand'ring from the fold of God;
Prone to love Thee, Lord, I feel it, Prone to serve the God I love;

## 104. Hallelujah For the Cross!

HORATIUS BONAR, arr.  
JAMES McGRANAHAN

1. The cross it stand-eth fast, Hal-le-lu-jah, hal-le-lu-jah! De-fy-ing ev-'ry blast, Hal-le-lu-jah, hal-le-lu-jah! The winds of hell have blown, The world its hate hath shown, Yet it is not o-ver-thrown, Hal-le-lu-jah for the cross!

2. It is the old cross still, Hal-le-lu-jah, hal-le-lu-jah! Its tri-umph let us tell, Hal-le-lu-jah, hal-le-lu-jah! The grace of God here shone Thro' Christ the bless-ed Son, Who did for sin a-tone, Hal-le-lu-jah for the cross!

3. 'Twas here the debt was paid, Hal-le-lu-jah, hal-le-lu-jah! Our sins on Je-sus laid, Hal-le-lu-jah, hal-le-lu-jah! So round the cross we sing Of Christ our of-fer-ing, Of Christ our liv-ing King, Hal-le-lu-jah for the cross!

OBBLIGATO DUET Sop. (or Ten.) and Alto  
Hal-le-lu-jah, hal-le-lu-jah, hal-le-

Soprano and Alto*  
CHORUS mp. Hal-le-lu-jah hal-le-lu-jah, hal-le-

Tenor and Bass

Copyright, 1910. Renewal. Hope Publishing Co., owner

# Hallelujah For the Cross!

lu - - jah for the cross! Hal - le - lu - jah,

lu - jah for the cross, hal-le-lu - jah for the cross! Hal - le - lu - jah,

hal - le - lu - jah, It shall nev - er suf - fer loss!

hal - le - lu - jah, It shall nev - er suf - fer, nev - er suf - fer loss!

**Full Chorus**

*Hal - le - lu - jah, hal - le - lu - jah, hal - le - lu - jah for the cross!

Hal - le - lu - jah, hal - le - lu - jah, It shall nev - er suf - fer loss!

*For a final ending, all the voices may sing the melody in unison through the last eight measures—the instrument playing the harmony.

## 105. Awakening Chorus

Charlotte G. Homer — Chas. H. Gabriel

1. A-wake! a-wake! and sing the bless-ed sto-ry; A-wake! a-wake! and let your song of praise a-rise; A-wake! a-wake! a-wake! the earth is full of glo-ry, And light is beam-ing from the ra-diant skies; The rocks and rills, the vales and hills re-sound with glad-ness, All na-ture joins to sing the triumph song. The Lord Je-

2. Ring out! ring out! O bells of joy and glad-ness! Re-peat, re-peat a-new the sto-ry o'er a-gain, Till all the earth shall lose its weight of sad-ness, And shout a-new the glo-ri-ous re-frain; With an-gels 'n the heights sing of the great sal-va-tion He wrest-ed from the hand of sin and death.

Copyright, 1905, by Chas. H. Gabriel. Hope Publishing Co., owner

# Awakening Chorus

ho-vah reigns and sin is back-ward hurled! Re-joice! re-joice! lift heart and voice, Je-ho-vah reigns!

*sin is back-ward hurled!*

**FULL HARMONY**

Pro-claim His sov-'reign pow'r to all the world, And let His glo-rious ban-ner be un-furled! Je-ho-vah reigns!

*pow'r to all the world, And let His grand and glo-rious ban-ner be un-furled! Je-ho-vah reigns! Je-ho-vah reigns!*

Re-joice! re-joice! re-joice! Je-ho-vah reigns!

*Re-joice! re-joice! re-joice!*

## 106. The Song of the Soldier

*"Thou therefore endure hardness, as a good soldier of Jesus Christ."* —Timothy 2: 3

Arr. from Falkner, 1723, by E. N.  
James McGranahan

1. Rise, ye chil-dren of sal-va-tion, All who cleave to Christ the Head;
2. Saints and he-roes long be-fore us Firm-ly on this ground have stood;
3. Deathless, we are all un-fear-ing, Life laid up with Christ in God;
4. Soon we all shall stand be-fore Him, See and know our glo-rious Lord;

Wake, a-rise! O might-y na-tion, Ere the foe on Zi-on tread.
See their ban-ners wav-ing o'er us, Con-quer-ors thro' Je-sus' blood.
In the morn of His ap-pear-ing Flow-eth forth a glo-ry flood.
Soon in joy and light a-dore Him, Each re-ceiv-ing his re-ward.

**Chorus** *m cres.*

Pour it forth a might-y an-them, Pour it forth a might-y an-them, Like the thun-ders of the sea;

Copyright, 1910. Renewal. Hope Publishing Co., owner

# The Song of the Soldier

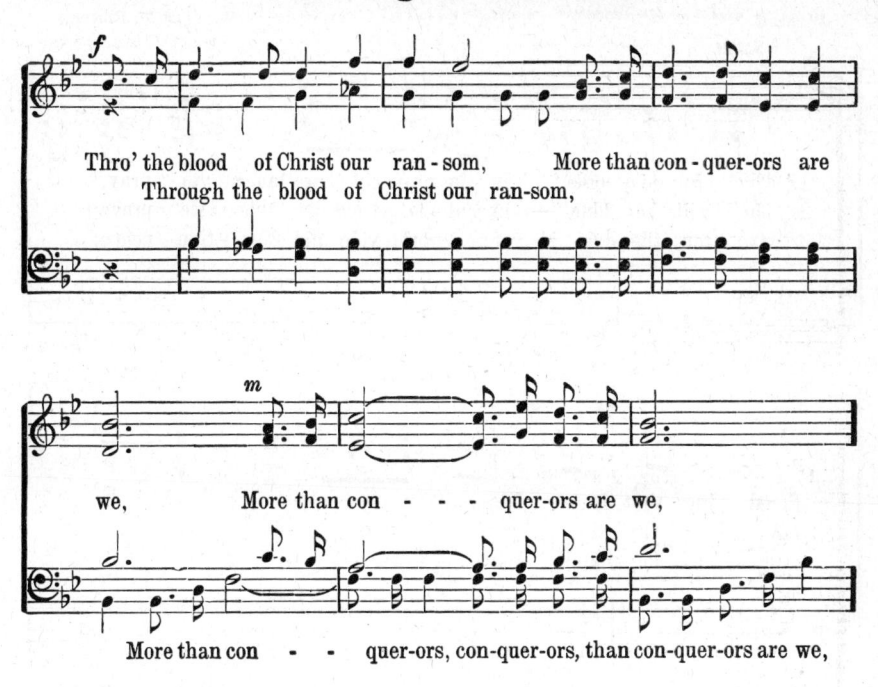

Thro' the blood of Christ our ran-som, More than con-quer-ors are we, More than con-quer-ors are we, More than con-quer-ors are we; Thro' the blood of Christ our ran-som, More than con-quer-ors are we.

Through the blood of Christ our ran-som, More than con-quer-ors, con-quer-ors, than con-quer-ors are we, More than con-quer-ors, con-quer-ors, than con-quer-ors are we;

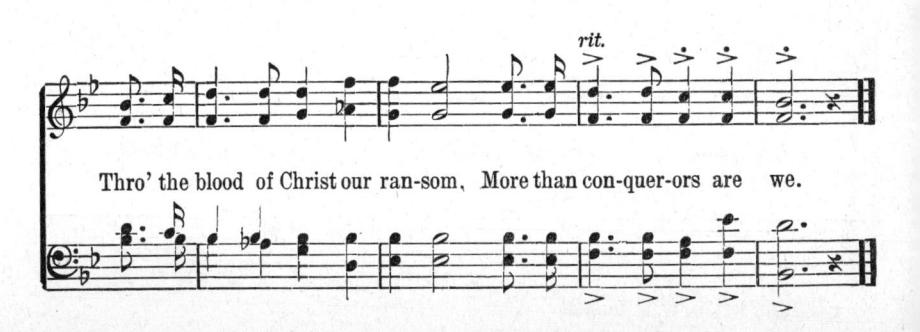

## 107. Thy Kingdom Come

W. M. R.  
William M. Runyan

Unison

1. "Thy king-dom come" is the prayer we are taught to pray,
2. "Thy will be done"— our al-le-giance by this we prove;
3. Has-ten the day of a world-wide and Chris-tian peace;

Plead-ing that Je - sus all na-tions of men shall sway;
Lov - ing Thy will, tow'rd the day of Thy pow'r we move;
Stretch forth Thy hand that the wars of the world may cease;

Thy king-dom come, do Thou has-ten the glo-rious day!
Yearn-ing to share in Thy king-dom of light and love;
Reign Thou in love that all cap-tives may find re-lease;

Thy king-dom come, O Lord, Thy king-dom come!
Thy king-dom come, O Lord, Thy king-dom come!
Thy king-dom come, O Lord, Thy king-dom come!

Copyright, 1921, by W. M. Runyan

# Thy Kingdom Come

**Chorus**

Thy kingdom come, 'midst the north-ern snows, Thy kingdom come, where the palm-tree grows; Far as the sun flings its glo-ri-ous ray, Where men are grop-ing to find the Way; Speed Thou Thy mes-sen-gers near and far, Led by the light of the Morn-ing Star:

**Parts**

That all the na-tions may know Thee and love Thee, Thy king-dom come!

# 108 Wonderful Grace of Jesus

H. L.  
Haldor Lillenas

1. Won-der-ful grace of Jesus, Great-er than all my sin;
2. Won-der-ful grace of Jesus, Reach-ing to all the lost,
3. Won-der-ful grace of Jesus, Reach-ing the most de-filed,

How shall my tongue de-scribe it, Where shall its praise be-gin?
By it I have been pardoned, Saved to the ut-ter-most,
By its trans-form-ing pow-er, Mak-ing him God's dear child,

Tak-ing a-way my bur-den, Set-ting my spir-it free;
Chains have been torn a-sun-der, Giv-ing me lib-er-ty;
Pur-chas-ing peace and heav-en, For all e-ter-ni-ty;

For the won-der-ful grace of Je-sus reach-es me.
For the won-der-ful grace of Je-sus reach-es me.
And the won-der-ful grace of Je-sus reach-es me.

**Chorus**

Won-der-ful the matchless grace of Je-sus, the matchless grace of Je-sus, Deep-er than the

Copyright, 1918. Hope Publishing Co., owner

# Wonderful Grace of Jesus

might-y roll-ing sea; the roll-ing sea; Won - - - der - ful
Higher than the mountain,
grace, all - suf - fi - - - cient for
spar-kling like a foun-tain, All - suf - fi - cient grace for e - ven
me, for e - ven me, Broad - er than the scope of my trans-
me,
gres - sions, Great - er far than all my sin and shame
gres-sions, sing it! my sin and shame,
O mag - ni - fy the pre-cious name of Je - sus, Praise His name!

## 109 All Hail, Immanuel

D. R. VAN SICKLE  
CHAS. H. GABRIEL

1. All hail to Thee, Im-man-u-el, We cast our crowns be-fore Thee;
2. All hail to Thee, Im-man-u-el, The ran-somed hosts surround Thee;
3. All hail to Thee, Im-man-u-el, Our ris-en King and Sav-ior!

Let ev-'ry heart o-bey Thy will, And ev-'ry voice a-
And earth-ly mon-archs clam-or forth Their Sov-'reign King to
Thy foes are van-quished, and Thou art Om-nip-o-tent for-

dore Thee. In praise to Thee, our Sav-ior King, The vi-brant
crown Thee. While those re-deemed in a-ges gone, As-sem-bled
ev-er. Death, sin and hell no lon-ger reign, And Sa-tan's

chords of Heav-en ring, And ech-o back the might-y strain:
round the great white throne, Break forth in-to im-mor-tal song:
pow'r is burst in twain; E-ter-nal glo-ry to Thy Name:

All hail! all hail! All hail! all hail! Im-man-u-el!
All hail! all hail!

Copyright, 1910, by E. O. Excell. Words and Music

# All Hail, Immanuel

# 110 Beloved, Now Are We

EL NATHAN  
JAMES McGRANAHAN

1. Sons of God, be-loved in Je-sus! O the won-drous word of grace;
   In His Son the Fa-ther sees us, And as sons He gives us place.
2. Bless-ed hope, now bright-ly beam-ing, On our God we soon shall gaze;
   And in light ce-les-tial gleam-ing, We shall see our Sav-ior's face.
3. By the pow'r of grace trans-form-ing, We shall then His im-age bear;
   Christ His prom-ised word per-form-ing, We shall then His glo-ry share.

CHORUS

"Be-lov-ed, now are we the sons of God, And it doth not yet ap-pear what we shall be; But we know . . . that when He shall ap-pear; . . . . . . We know . . that when He shall ap-pear;
But we know, we know, we know that when He shall ap-pear; We know, we know, we

Copyright, 1903. Hope Publishing Co., owner

## Beloved, Now Are We

pear, . . . . . . . We shall be like Him, we shall be
know that when He shall ap-pear,

like Him, For we shall see . . Him as . . . He is." . . .

**111**  I'll Live For Him

R. E. Hudson

C. R. Dunbar

1. My life, my love I give to Thee, Thou Lamb of God who died for me;
2. I now be-lieve Thou dost re-ceive, For Thou hast died that I might live;
3. O Thou who died on Cal-va-ry, To save my soul and make me free,

Cho.—I'll live for Him who died for me, How hap-py then my life shall be!

D. C. Chorus

Oh, may I ev-er faith-ful be, My Sav-ior and my God!
And now hence-forth I'll trust in Thee, My Sav-ior and my God!
I'll con-se-crate my life to Thee, My Sav-ior and my God!

I'll live for Him who died for me, My Sav-ior and my God!

Copyright, 1918. Renewal. Mrs. Mary Hudson, owner

## 112  All Hail the Power

OLIVER HOLDEN

1. All hail the pow'r of Jesus' name! Let angels prostrate fall;
2. Ye chosen seed of Israel's race, Ye ransomed from the fall,
3. Let ev'ry kindred, ev'ry tribe On this terrestrial ball,

Bring forth the royal diadem, And crown Him Lord of all,
Hail Him who saves you by His grace, And crown Him Lord of all,
To Him all majesty ascribe, And crown Him Lord of all,

Bring forth the royal diadem, And crown Him Lord of all!
Hail Him who saves you by His grace, And crown Him Lord of all!
To Him all majesty ascribe, And crown Him Lord of all!

## 113

[SECOND TUNE]  Miles' Lane. C. M.

WILLIAM SHRUBSOLE

1. All hail the pow'r of Jesus' name! Let angels prostrate fall; Bring forth the royal diadem, And crown Him, crown Him, crown Him, Crown Him Lord of all!

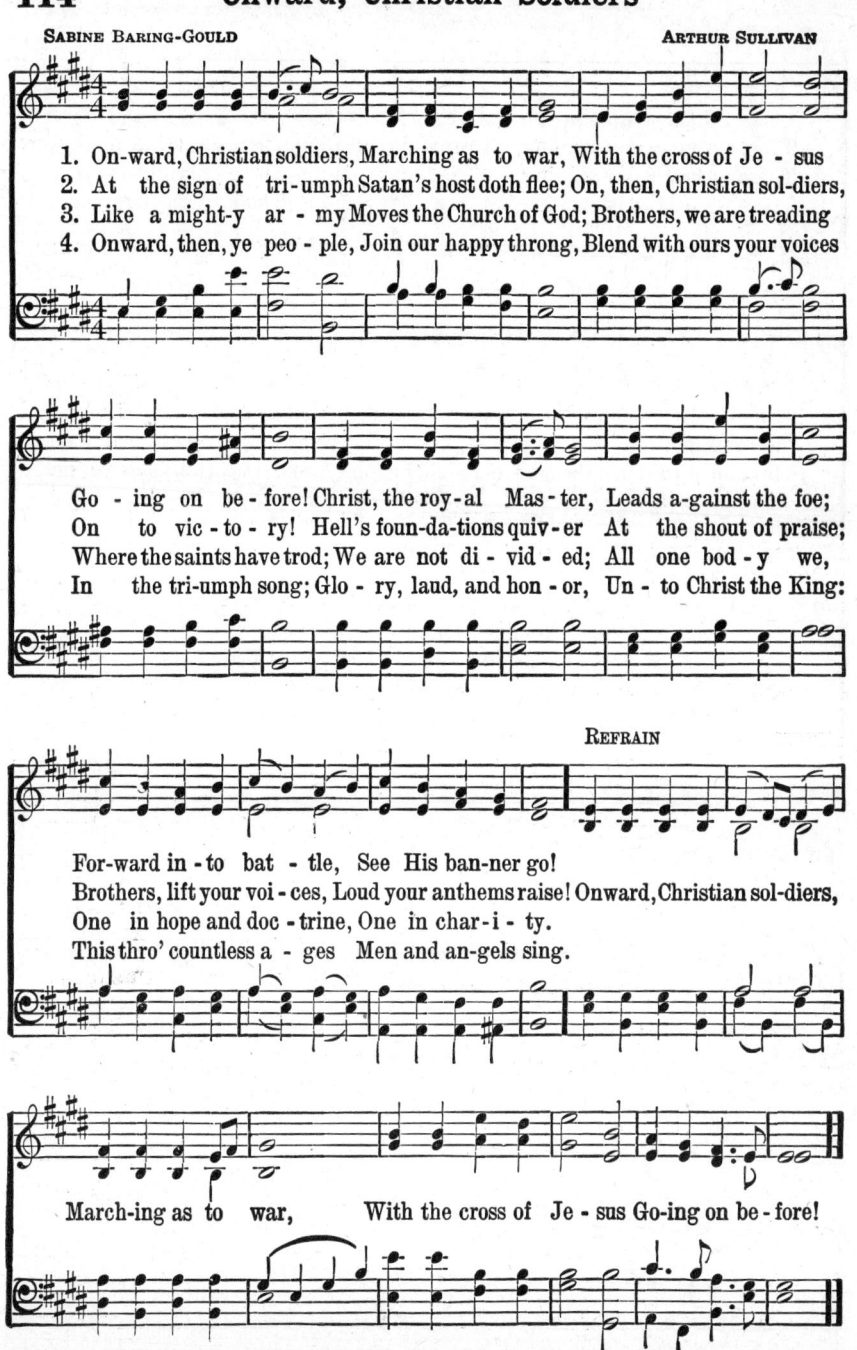

# 114 Onward, Christian Soldiers

SABINE BARING-GOULD  ARTHUR SULLIVAN

1. On-ward, Christian soldiers, Marching as to war, With the cross of Je - sus
2. At the sign of tri-umph Satan's host doth flee; On, then, Christian sol-diers,
3. Like a might-y ar - my Moves the Church of God; Brothers, we are treading
4. Onward, then, ye peo - ple, Join our happy throng, Blend with ours your voices

Go - ing on be - fore! Christ, the roy-al Mas - ter, Leads a-gainst the foe;
On to vic - to - ry! Hell's foun-da-tions quiv-er At the shout of praise;
Where the saints have trod; We are not di - vid - ed; All one bod - y we,
In the tri-umph song; Glo - ry, laud, and hon - or, Un - to Christ the King:

**REFRAIN**

For-ward in - to bat - tle, See His ban-ner go!
Brothers, lift your voi - ces, Loud your anthems raise! Onward, Christian sol-diers,
One in hope and doc - trine, One in char - i - ty.
This thro' countless a - ges Men and an-gels sing.

March-ing as to war, With the cross of Je - sus Go-ing on be - fore!

## 115 There's a Great Day Coming

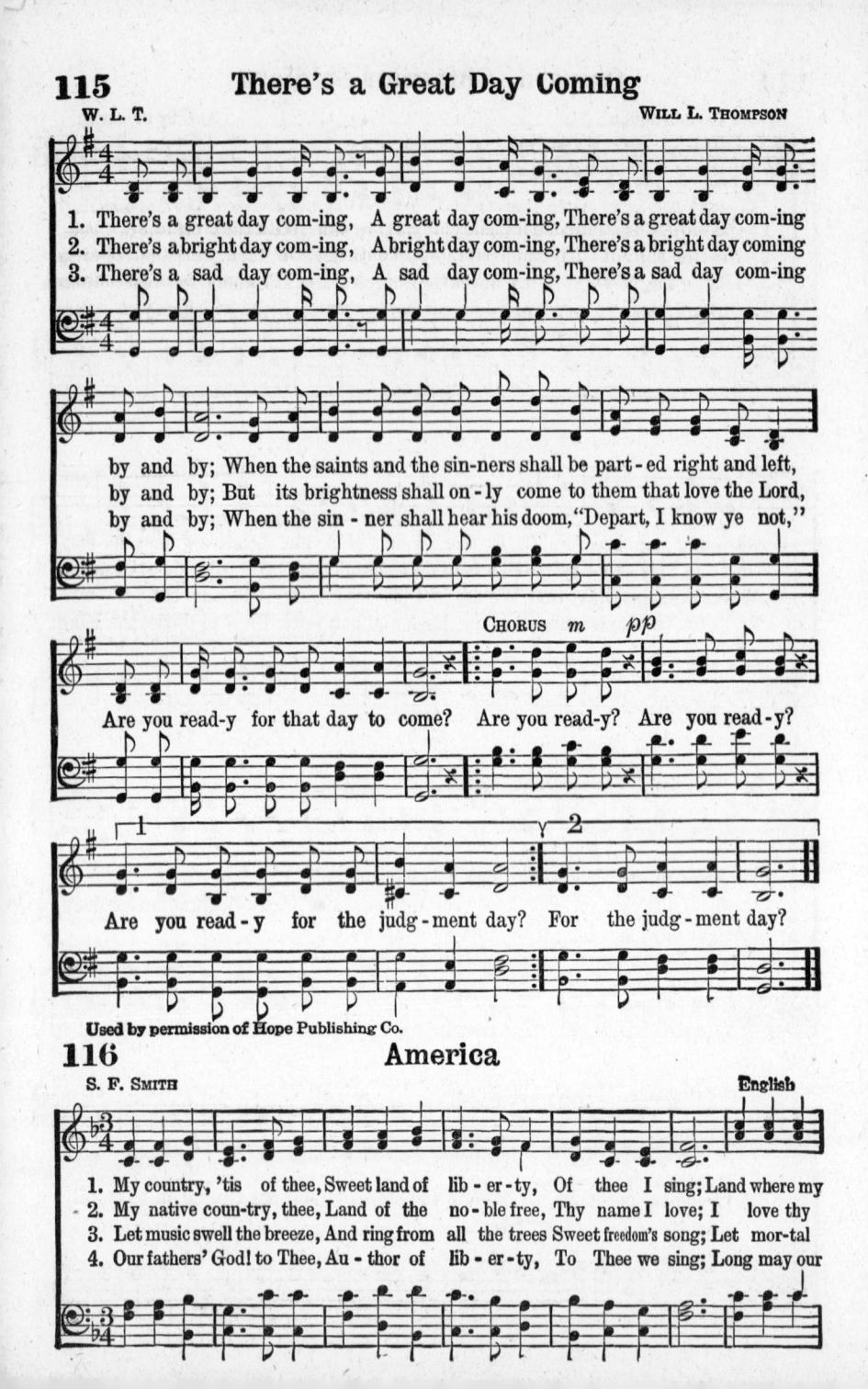

W. L. T.     Will L. Thompson

1. There's a great day com-ing, A great day com-ing, There's a great day com-ing
2. There's a bright day com-ing, A bright day com-ing, There's a bright day coming
3. There's a sad day com-ing, A sad day com-ing, There's a sad day com-ing

by and by; When the saints and the sin-ners shall be part-ed right and left,
by and by; But its brightness shall on-ly come to them that love the Lord,
by and by; When the sin-ner shall hear his doom, "Depart, I know ye not,"

CHORUS   *m*   *pp*

Are you read-y for that day to come? Are you read-y? Are you read-y?

Are you read-y for the judg-ment day? For the judg-ment day?

Used by permission of Hope Publishing Co.

## 116 America

S. F. Smith     English

1. My country, 'tis of thee, Sweet land of lib-er-ty, Of thee I sing; Land where my
2. My native coun-try, thee, Land of the no-ble free, Thy name I love; I love thy
3. Let music swell the breeze, And ring from all the trees Sweet freedom's song; Let mor-tal
4. Our fathers' God! to Thee, Au-thor of lib-er-ty, To Thee we sing; Long may our

## America

fa - thers died, Land of the pilgrims' pride, From ev-'ry mountain side Let free-dom ring!
rocks and rills, Thy woods and templed hills; My heart with rapture thrills Like that a-bove.
tongues awake; Let all that breathe partake; Let rocks their silence break, The sound pro-long.
land be bright With freedom's ho-ly light; Pro-tect us by Thy might, Great God, our King.

## 117 America the Beautiful

KATHERINE LEE BATES  
SAMUEL A. WARD

1. O beau-ti-ful for spacious skies, For am-ber waves of grain, For pur-ple mountain
2. O beau-ti-ful for pil-grim feet, Whose stern, impassioned stress A thor-ough-fare for
3. O beau-ti-ful for he-roes proved In lib-er a- -ing strife, Who more than self their
4. O beau-ti-ful for patriot dream That sees beyond the years Thine al-a-bas-ter

maj-es-ties A-bove the fruit-ed plain! A-mer-i-ca! A-mer-i-ca! God
free-dom beat A-cross the wil-der-ness! A-mer-i-ca! A-mer-i-ca! God
coun-try loved, And mer-cy more than life! A-mer-i-ca! A-mer-i-ca! May
cit-ies gleam, Undimmed by hu-man tears! A-mer-i-ca! A-mer-i-ca! God

shed His grace on thee, And crown thy good with brother-hood From sea to shin-ing sea!
mend thine ev-'ry flaw, Con-firm thy soul in self-con-trol, Thy lib-er-ty in law!
God thy gold re-fine, Till all suc-cess be no-ble-ness, And ev-'ry gain di-vine!
shed His grace on thee, And crown thy good with brother-hood From sea to shin-ing sea!

# 118 Jesus Is Calling

FANNY J. CROSBY  
GEO. C. STEBBINS

1. Je-sus is ten-der-ly call-ing thee home—Call-ing to-day,
2. Je-sus is call-ing the wea-ry to rest—Call-ing to-day,
3. Je-sus is wait-ing; O come to Him now—Wait-ing to-day,
4. Je-sus is plead-ing; O list to His voice: Hear Him to-day,

call-ing to-day; Why from the sun-shine of love wilt thou roam
call-ing to-day; Bring Him thy bur-den and thou shalt be blest:
wait-ing to-day; Come with thy sins; at His feet low-ly bow;
hear Him to-day; They who be-lieve on His name shall re-joice;

Far-ther and far-ther a-way?
He will not turn thee a-way.
Come, and no lon-ger de-lay.
Quick-ly a-rise and a-way.

**REFRAIN**

Call - - ing to-day, . . . . Call - - ing to-day, . . . .
Call-ing, call-ing to-day, to-day, Call-ing, call-ing to-day, to-day,

Je - - - sus is call - - - ing,
call-ing to-day, is ten-der-ly call-ing to-day.

Copyright, 1911, by Geo. C. Stebbins. Renewal. Hope Publishing Company, owner

## Softly and Tenderly

W. L. T.  
Will L. Thompson

1. Soft-ly and ten-der-ly Je-sus is call-ing, Call-ing for you and for me;
2. Why should we tarry when Jesus is plead-ing, Pleading for you and for me?
3. Time is now fleeting, the moments are passing, Passing from you and from me;
4. Oh! for the won-der-ful love He has promised, Promised for you and for me;

See, on the portals He's waiting and watching, Watching for you and for me.
Why should we linger and heed not His mercies, Mer-cies for you and for me?
Shadows are gathering, death-beds are coming, Com-ing for you and for me.
Tho' we have sinned, He has mercy and pardon, Par-don for you and for me.

CHORUS

Come home,.. come home,...... Ye who are wear-y, come home;...
Come home, come home,

Ear-nest-ly, ten-der-ly, Je-sus is call-ing, Call-ing, O sin-ner, come home!

Hope Publishing Co., owners. Used by permission.

# 120 Let Jesus Come Into Your Heart

C. H. M.  
Mrs. C. H. Morris

1. If you are tired of the load of your sin, Let Jesus come into your heart; If you desire a new life to begin,
2. If 'tis for purity now that you sigh, Let Jesus come into your heart; Fountains for cleansing are flowing near by,
3. If there's a tempest your voice cannot still, Let Jesus come into your heart; If there's a void this world never can fill,
4. If you would join the glad songs of the blest, Let Jesus come into your heart; If you would enter the mansions of rest,

Let Jesus come into your heart.

**Chorus**

Just now, your doubtings give o'er; Just now, reject Him no more; Just now, throw open the door; Let Jesus come into your heart.

Copyright, 1926. Renewal. Hope Publishing Co., owner

## 121. Seeking the Lost

W. A. O.  
W. A. Odgen

1. Seek-ing the lost, yes, kind-ly en-treat-ing Wan-der-ers on the moun-tain a-stray; "Come un-to Me," His mes-sage re-peat-ing, Words of the Mas-ter speak-ing to-day.
2. Seek-ing the lost, and point-ing to Je-sus, Souls that are weak and hearts that are sore; Lead-ing them forth in ways of sal-va-tion, Show-ing the path to life ev-er-more.
3. Thus I would go on mis-sions of mer-cy, Fol-low-ing Christ from day un-to day; Cheer-ing the faint, and rais-ing the fall-en; Point-ing the lost to Je-sus, the Way.

**Chorus**

Go-ing a-far upon the moun-tain,  
In-to the fold of my Re-deem-er,  
Go-ing a-far . . . . . up-on the moun-tain, . . . Bring-ing the  
In-to the fold . . . . . of my Re-deem-er, . . . Je-sus, the

Bring-ing the wan-d'rer back a-gain,  
Je-sus, the Lamb for sin-ners (*Omit.*) . . . . slain, for sinners slain.  
wan - - - d'rer back a-gain, . . . . .  
Lamb . . . . . for sin-ners (*Omit.*) . . . . slain. . . . . .

Used by permission of Mrs. W. A. Ogden.

## 122. Jesus, I Come

W. T. Sleeper
Geo. C. Stebbins

1. Out of my bond-age, sor-row and night, Je-sus, I come, Je-sus, I come;
2. Out of my shame-ful fail-ure and loss, Je-sus, I come, Je-sus, I come;
3. Out of un-rest and ar-ro-gant pride, Je-sus, I come, Je-sus, I come;
4. Out of the fear and dread of the tomb, Je-sus, I come, Je-sus, I come;

In-to Thy free-dom, glad-ness and light, Je-sus, I come to Thee;
In-to the glo-rious gain of Thy cross, Je-sus, I come to Thee;
In-to Thy bless-ed will to a-bide, Je-sus, I come to Thee;
In-to the joy and light of Thy home, Je-sus, I come to Thee;

Out of my sick-ness in-to Thy health, Out of my want and in-to Thy wealth,
Out of earth's sorrows in-to Thy balm, Out of life's storms and in-to Thy calm,
Out of my-self to dwell in Thy love, Out of de-spair in-to rap-tures a-bove,
Out of the depths of ru-in un-told, In-to the peace of Thy sheltering fold,

Out of my sin and in-to Thy-self, Je-sus, I come to Thee.
Out of dis-tress to ju-bi-lant psalm, Je-sus, I come to Thee.
Up-ward for aye on wings like a dove, Je-sus, I come to Thee.
Ev-er Thy glo-rious face to be-hold, Je-sus, I come to Thee.

Copyright, 1914, by Geo. C. Stebbins. Renewal. Hope Publishing Company, owner

## 123 Why Not Now?

El Nathan  
C. C. Case

1. While we pray and while we plead, While you see your soul's deep need,
2. You have wan-dered far a-way; Do not risk an-oth-er day;
3. In the world you've failed to find Aught of peace for troub-led mind;
4. Come to Christ, con-fes-sion make; Come to Christ, and par-don take;

While our Fa-ther calls you home, Will you not, my broth-er, come?
Do not turn from God thy face, But to-day ac-cept His grace.
Come to Christ, on Him be-lieve, Peace and joy you shall re-ceive.
Trust in Him from day to day, He will keep you all the way.

**Chorus**

Why not now?... Why not now?... Why not come to Je-sus now?
Why not now? Why not now?

Why not now?... Why not now?... Why not come to Je-sus now?
Why not now? Why not now?

Copyright, 1891, by C. C. Case

## 124. Here Am I, Send Me

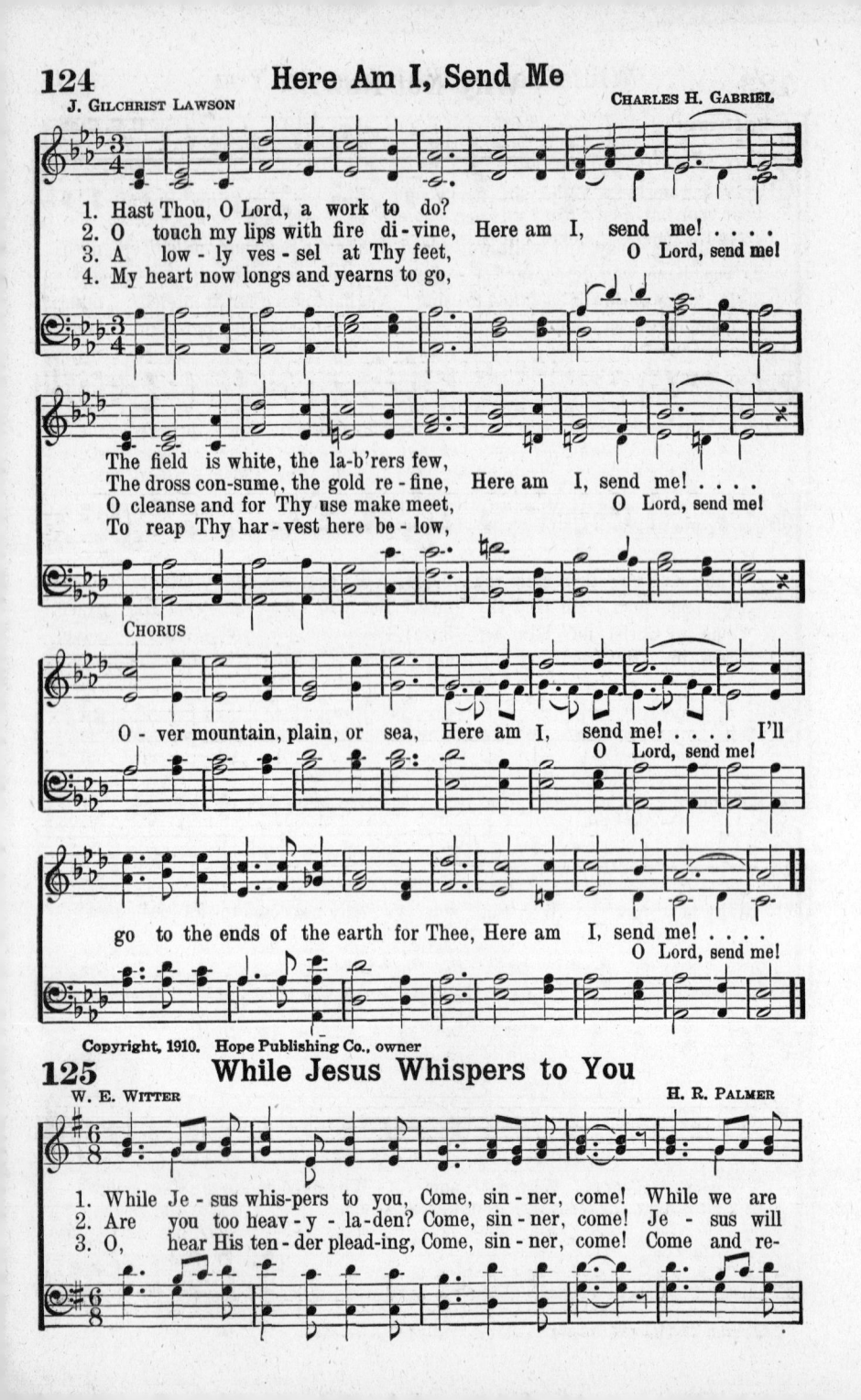

J. Gilchrist Lawson — Charles H. Gabriel

1. Hast Thou, O Lord, a work to do?
2. O touch my lips with fire di-vine,
3. A low-ly ves-sel at Thy feet,
4. My heart now longs and yearns to go,

The field is white, the la-b'rers few,
The dross con-sume, the gold re-fine,
O cleanse and for Thy use make meet,
To reap Thy har-vest here be-low,

Here am I, send me! .... O Lord, send me!

CHORUS

O-ver mountain, plain, or sea, Here am I, send me! .... I'll go to the ends of the earth for Thee, Here am I, send me! .... O Lord, send me!

Copyright, 1910. Hope Publishing Co., owner

## 125. While Jesus Whispers to You

W. E. Witter — H. R. Palmer

1. While Je-sus whis-pers to you, Come, sin-ner, come! While we are
2. Are you too heav-y-la-den? Come, sin-ner, come! Je-sus will
3. O, hear His ten-der plead-ing, Come, sin-ner, come! Come and re-

## While Jesus Whispers to You

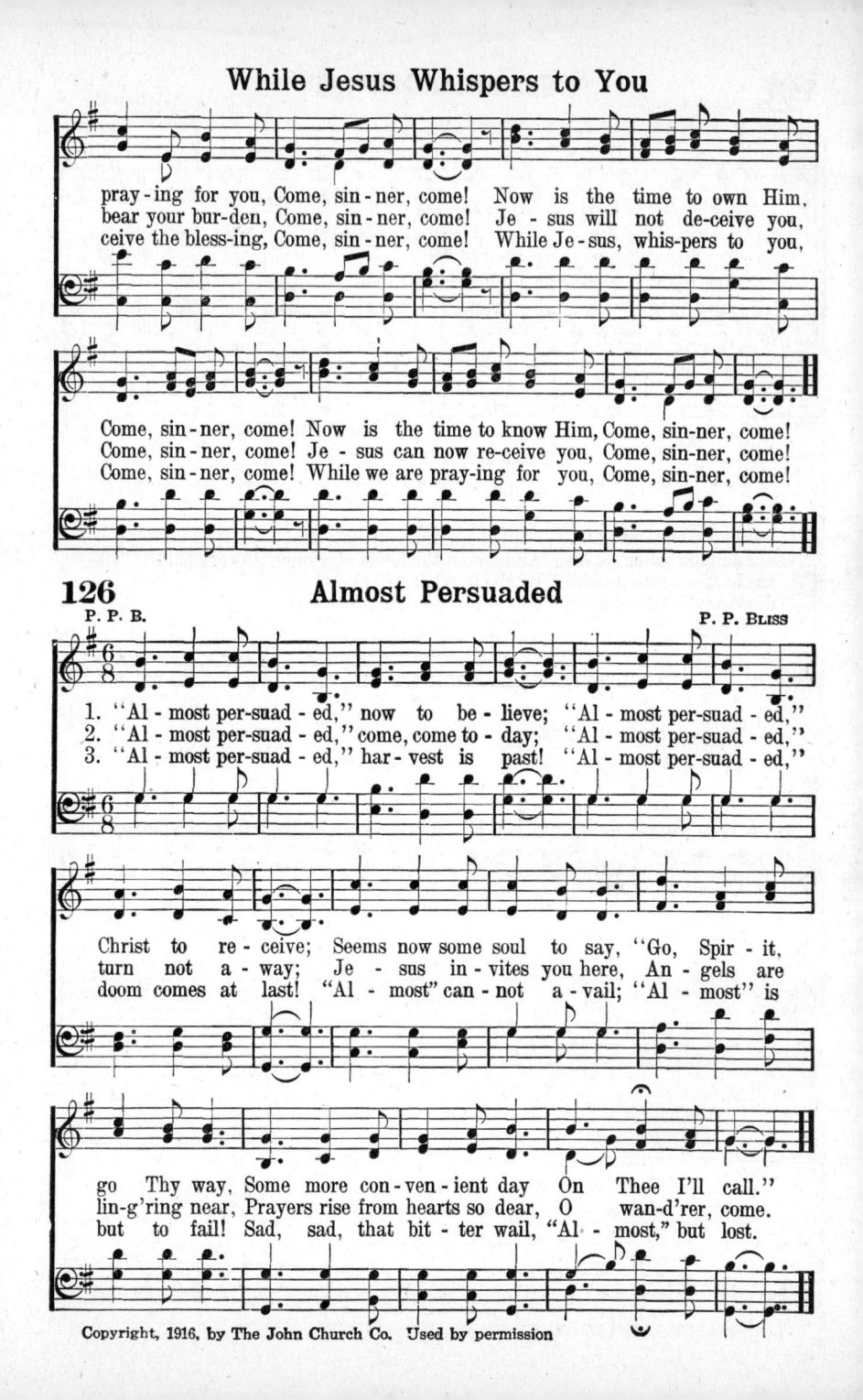

pray-ing for you, Come, sin-ner, come! Now is the time to own Him,
bear your bur-den, Come, sin-ner, come! Je - sus will not de-ceive you,
ceive the bless-ing, Come, sin-ner, come! While Je-sus, whis-pers to you,

Come, sin-ner, come! Now is the time to know Him, Come, sin-ner, come!
Come, sin-ner, come! Je - sus can now re-ceive you, Come, sin-ner, come!
Come, sin-ner, come! While we are pray-ing for you, Come, sin-ner, come!

### 126 Almost Persuaded

P. P. B.                                          P. P. Bliss

1. "Al - most per-suad - ed," now to be - lieve; "Al - most per-suad - ed,"
2. "Al - most per-suad - ed," come, come to - day; "Al - most per-suad - ed,"
3. "Al - most per-suad - ed," har - vest is past! "Al - most per-suad - ed,"

Christ to re - ceive; Seems now some soul to say, "Go, Spir - it,
turn not a - way; Je - sus in - vites you here, An - gels are
doom comes at last! "Al - most" can - not a - vail; "Al - most" is

go Thy way, Some more con-ven-ient day On Thee I'll call."
lin-g'ring near, Prayers rise from hearts so dear, O wan-d'rer, come.
but to fail! Sad, sad, that bit - ter wail, "Al - most," but lost.

Copyright, 1916, by The John Church Co. Used by permission

## 127  Jesus Paid It All

Mrs. H. M. Hall  
John T. Grape

1. I hear the Sav-ior say, "Thy strength in-deed is small, Child of weakness, watch and pray, Find in Me thine all in all."
2. Lord, now in-deed I find Thy pow'r, and Thine a-lone, Can change the lep-er's spots, And melt the heart of stone.
3. For noth-ing good have I Where-by Thy grace to claim— I'll wash my garments white In the blood of Cal-v'ry's Lamb.
4. And when, be-fore the throne, I stand in Him com-plete, "Je-sus died my soul to save," My lips shall still re-peat.

CHORUS

Je-sus paid it all, All to Him I owe; Sin had left a crimson stain, He washed it white as snow.

## 128  Where He Leads Me

E. W. Blandly  
J. S. Norris

1. I can hear my Sav-ior call-ing, I can hear my Sav-ior call-ing,
2. I'll go with Him thro' the gar-den, I'll go with Him thro' the gar-den,
3. I'll go with Him thro' the judg-ment, I'll go with Him thro' the judg-ment,
4. He will give me grace and glo-ry, He will give me grace and glo-ry,

REF.—Where He leads me I will fol-low, Where He leads me I will fol-low,

Copyright, 1890, by J. S. Norris. Used by permission

## Where He Leads Me

I can hear my Sav-ior call-ing, "Take thy cross and fol-low, fol-low Me."
I'll go with Him thro' the gar-den, I'll go with Him, with Him all the way.
I'll go with Him thro' the judg-ment, I'll go with Him, with Him all the way.
He will give me grace and glo-ry, And go with me, with me all the way.

Where He leads me I will fol-low, I'll go with Him, with Him all the way.

## 129 Lord, I'm Coming Home

W. J. K.     WM. J. KIRKPATRICK

1. I've wan-dered far a-way from God, Now I'm com-ing home;
2. I've wast-ed man-y pre-cious years, Now I'm com-ing home;
3. I've tired of sin and stray-ing, Lord, Now I'm com-ing home;
4. My soul is sick, my heart is sore, Now I'm com-ing home;

The paths of sin too long I've trod, Lord, I'm com-ing home.
I now re-pent with bit-ter tears, Lord, I'm com-ing home.
I'll trust Thy love, be-lieve Thy word, Lord, I'm com-ing home.
My strength re-new, my hope re-store, Lord, I'm com-ing home.

D. S.—O-pen wide Thine arms of love, Lord, I'm com-ing home.

CHORUS     D. S.

Com-ing home, com-ing home, Nev-er-more to roam,

Copyright, 1920, by Wm. J. Kirkpatrick. Renewal. Hope Publishing Company, owner

## 130. Just As I Am

CHARLOTTE ELLIOTT  
WILLIAM B. BRADBURY

1. Just as I am, without one plea, But that Thy blood was shed for me, And that Thou bidd'st me come to Thee, O Lamb of God, I come! I come!
2. Just as I am, and waiting not To rid my soul of one dark blot, To Thee whose blood can cleanse each spot, O Lamb of God, I come! I come!
3. Just as I am, tho' tossed about With many a conflict, many a doubt, Fightings and fears within, without, O Lamb of God, I come! I come!
4. Just as I am—poor, wretched, blind; Sight, riches, healing of the mind, Yea, all I need in Thee to find, O Lamb of God, I come! I come!
5. Just as I am—Thou wilt receive, Wilt welcome, pardon, cleanse relieve; Because Thy promise I believe, O Lamb of God, I come! I come!

## 131. I Am Coming, Lord

L. H.  
L. HARTSOUGH

1. I hear Thy welcome voice, That calls me, Lord, to Thee, For cleansing in Thy precious blood That flowed on Calvary.
2. Tho' coming weak and vile, Thou dost my strength assure; Thou dost my vileness fully cleanse, Till spotless all and pure.
3. 'Tis Jesus calls me on To perfect faith and love, To perfect hope, and peace, and trust, For earth and Heav'n above.

CHORUS

I am coming, Lord! Coming now to

Used by permission

# I Am Coming, Lord

Thee! Wash me, cleanse me in the blood That flowed on Cal-va-ry!

## 132  Bring Them In

ALEXCENAH THOMAS — W. A. OGDEN

1. Hark! 'tis the Shepherd's voice I hear, Out in the des-ert dark and drear,
2. Who'll go and help this Shepherd kind, Help Him the wand'ring ones to find?
3. Out in the des-ert hear their cry, Out on the mountains wild and high;

Call-ing the sheep who've gone a-stray Far from the Shepherd's fold a-way.
Who'll bring the lost ones to the fold, Where they'll be sheltered from the cold?
Hark! 'tis the Mas-ter speaks to thee, "Go find my sheep wher-e'er they be."

**CHORUS**

Bring them in, bring them in, Bring them in from the fields of sin;
Bring them in, bring them in, Bring the wand'ring ones to Je-sus.

Copyright, 1885, by W. A. Ogden. Used by permission

## 133. Glory to His Name

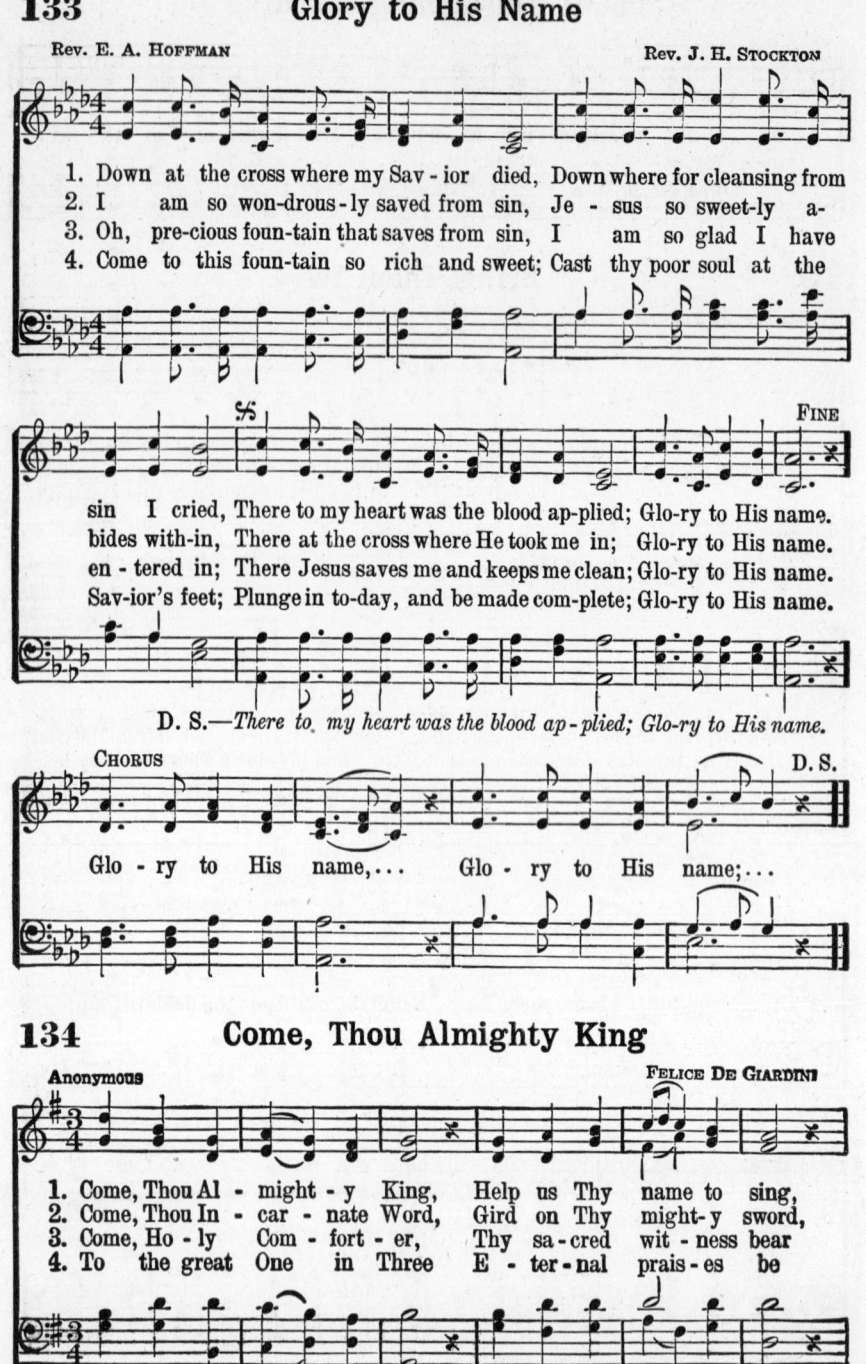

Rev. E. A. Hoffman  
Rev. J. H. Stockton

1. Down at the cross where my Sav-ior died, Down where for cleansing from
2. I am so won-drous-ly saved from sin, Je - sus so sweet-ly a-
3. Oh, pre-cious foun-tain that saves from sin, I am so glad I have
4. Come to this foun-tain so rich and sweet; Cast thy poor soul at the

sin I cried, There to my heart was the blood ap-plied; Glo-ry to His name.  
bides with-in, There at the cross where He took me in; Glo-ry to His name.  
en - tered in; There Jesus saves me and keeps me clean; Glo-ry to His name.  
Sav-ior's feet; Plunge in to-day, and be made com-plete; Glo-ry to His name.

D. S.—There to my heart was the blood ap - plied; Glo-ry to His name.

CHORUS

Glo - ry to His name,... Glo - ry to His name;...

## 134. Come, Thou Almighty King

Anonymous  
Felice De Giardini

1. Come, Thou Al - might-y King, Help us Thy name to sing,
2. Come, Thou In - car - nate Word, Gird on Thy might-y sword,
3. Come, Ho - ly Com - fort - er, Thy sa - cred wit - ness bear
4. To the great One in Three E - ter - nal prais - es be

## Come, Thou Almighty King

Help us to praise: Fa-ther, all-glo-ri-ous, O'er all vic-
Our prayer at-tend: Come, and Thy peo-ple bless, And give Thy
In this glad hour: Thou who al-might-y art, Now rule in
Hence ev-er-more. His sov-'reign maj-es-ty May we in

to-ri-ous, Come, and reign o-ver us, An-cient of Days.
word suc-cess: Spir-it of ho-li-ness, On us de-scend.
ev-'ry heart, And ne'er from us de-part, Spir-it of pow'r.
glo-ry see, And to e-ter-ni-ty Love and a-dore.

### 135  Alas! and Did My Savior Bleed?

ISAAC WATTS  HUGH WILSON

1. A-las! and did my Sav-ior bleed? And did my Sov-'reign die?
2. Was it for crimes that I have done He groaned up-on the tree?
3. Well might the sun in dark-ness hide, And shut his glo-ries in,
4. But drops of grief can ne'er re-pay The debt of love I owe;

Would He de-vote that sa-cred head For such a worm as I?
A-maz-ing pit-y! grace un-known! And love be-yond de-gree!
When Christ, the might-y Mak-er, died For man the crea-ture's sin.
Here, Lord, I give my-self to Thee,—'Tis all that I can do.

## 136. Near the Cross

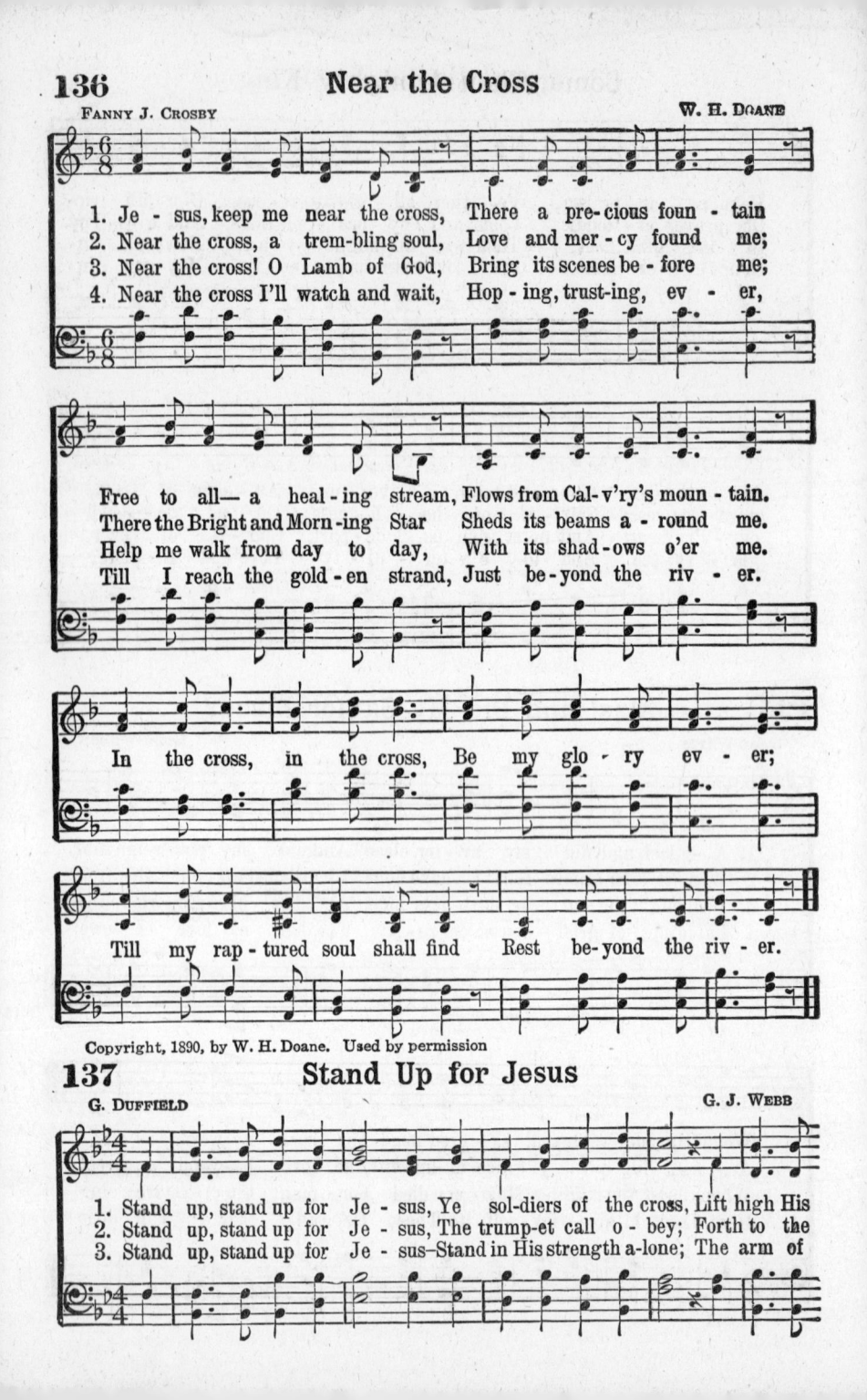

FANNY J. CROSBY  
W. H. DOANE

1. Je - sus, keep me near the cross, There a pre - cious foun - tain
2. Near the cross, a trem - bling soul, Love and mer - cy found me;
3. Near the cross! O Lamb of God, Bring its scenes be - fore me;
4. Near the cross I'll watch and wait, Hop - ing, trust - ing, ev - er,

Free to all— a heal - ing stream, Flows from Cal - v'ry's moun - tain.
There the Bright and Morn - ing Star Sheds its beams a - round me.
Help me walk from day to day, With its shad - ows o'er me.
Till I reach the gold - en strand, Just be - yond the riv - er.

In the cross, in the cross, Be my glo - ry ev - er;

Till my rap - tured soul shall find Rest be - yond the riv - er.

Copyright, 1890, by W. H. Doane. Used by permission.

## 137. Stand Up for Jesus

G. DUFFIELD  
G. J. WEBB

1. Stand up, stand up for Je - sus, Ye sol - diers of the cross, Lift high His
2. Stand up, stand up for Je - sus, The trump - et call o - bey; Forth to the
3. Stand up, stand up for Je - sus—Stand in His strength a - lone; The arm of

## Stand Up for Jesus

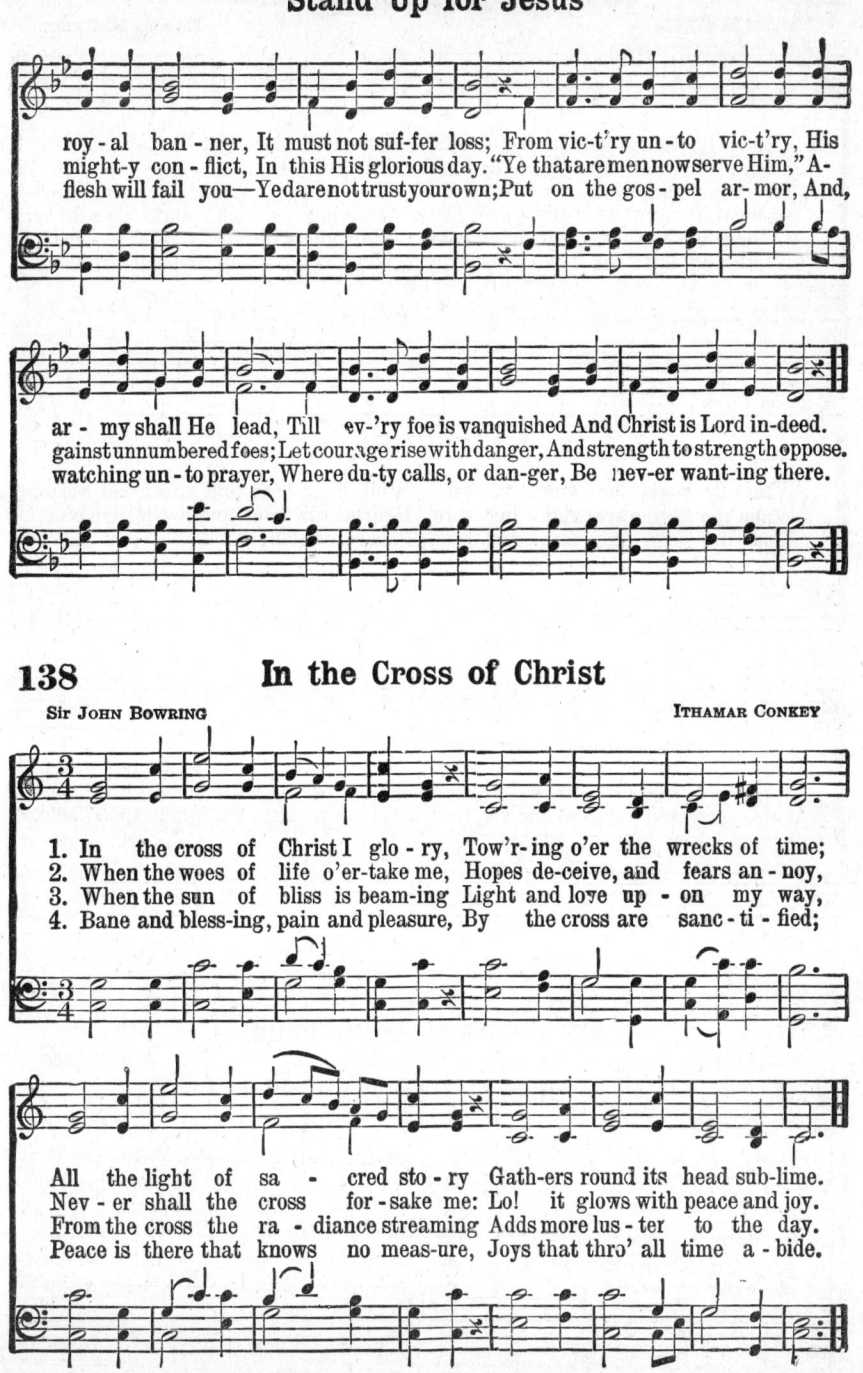

roy - al ban - ner, It must not suf-fer loss; From vic-t'ry un - to vic-t'ry, His
might-y con - flict, In this His glorious day. "Ye that are men now serve Him," A-
flesh will fail you—Ye dare not trust your own; Put on the gos - pel ar - mor, And,

ar - my shall He lead, Till ev-'ry foe is vanquished And Christ is Lord in-deed.
gainst unnumbered foes; Let courage rise with danger, And strength to strength oppose.
watching un - to prayer, Where du-ty calls, or dan-ger, Be nev-er want-ing there.

**138**  **In the Cross of Christ**

Sir JOHN BOWRING  ITHAMAR CONKEY

1. In the cross of Christ I glo - ry, Tow'r-ing o'er the wrecks of time;
2. When the woes of life o'er-take me, Hopes de-ceive, and fears an - noy,
3. When the sun of bliss is beam-ing Light and love up - on my way,
4. Bane and bless-ing, pain and pleasure, By the cross are sanc - ti - fied;

All the light of sa - cred sto - ry Gath-ers round its head sub-lime.
Nev - er shall the cross for - sake me: Lo! it glows with peace and joy.
From the cross the ra - diance streaming Adds more lus - ter to the day.
Peace is there that knows no meas-ure, Joys that thro' all time a - bide.

## 139. Holy Spirit, Faithful Guide

MARCUS M. WELLS     MARCUS M. WELLS

1. Ho - ly Spir - it, faith - ful Guide, Ev - er near the Chris-tian's side;
   Gen - tly lead us by the hand, Pil - grims in a des - ert land;
2. Ev - er pres - ent, tru - est Friend, Ev - er near Thine aid to lend,
   Leave us not to doubt and fear, Grop-ing on in dark - ness drear;
3. When our days of toil shall cease, Wait-ing still for sweet re - lease,
   Noth-ing left but heav'n and prayer, Wond'ring if our names were there;

Wea - ry souls for - e'er re - joice, While they hear that sweet - est voice,
When the storms are rag - ing sore, Hearts grow faint, and hopes give o'er,
Wad - ing deep the dis - mal flood, Plead-ing naught but Je - sus' blood,

Whis-p'ring soft - ly, "Wand'rer, come! Fol - low Me, I'll guide thee home."
Whis - per soft - ly, "Wand'rer, come! Fol - low Me, I'll guide thee home."
Whis - per soft - ly, "Wand'rer, come! Fol - low Me, I'll guide thee home."

## 140. My Jesus, I Love Thee

Anonymous     A. J. GORDON

1. My Je - sus, I love Thee, I know Thou art mine, For Thee all the
2. I love Thee, be - cause Thou hast first lov - ed me, And pur-chased my
3. I'll love Thee in life, I will love Thee in death, And praise Thee in
4. In man-sions of glo - ry and end-less de - light, I'll ev - er a -

## My Jesus, I Love Thee

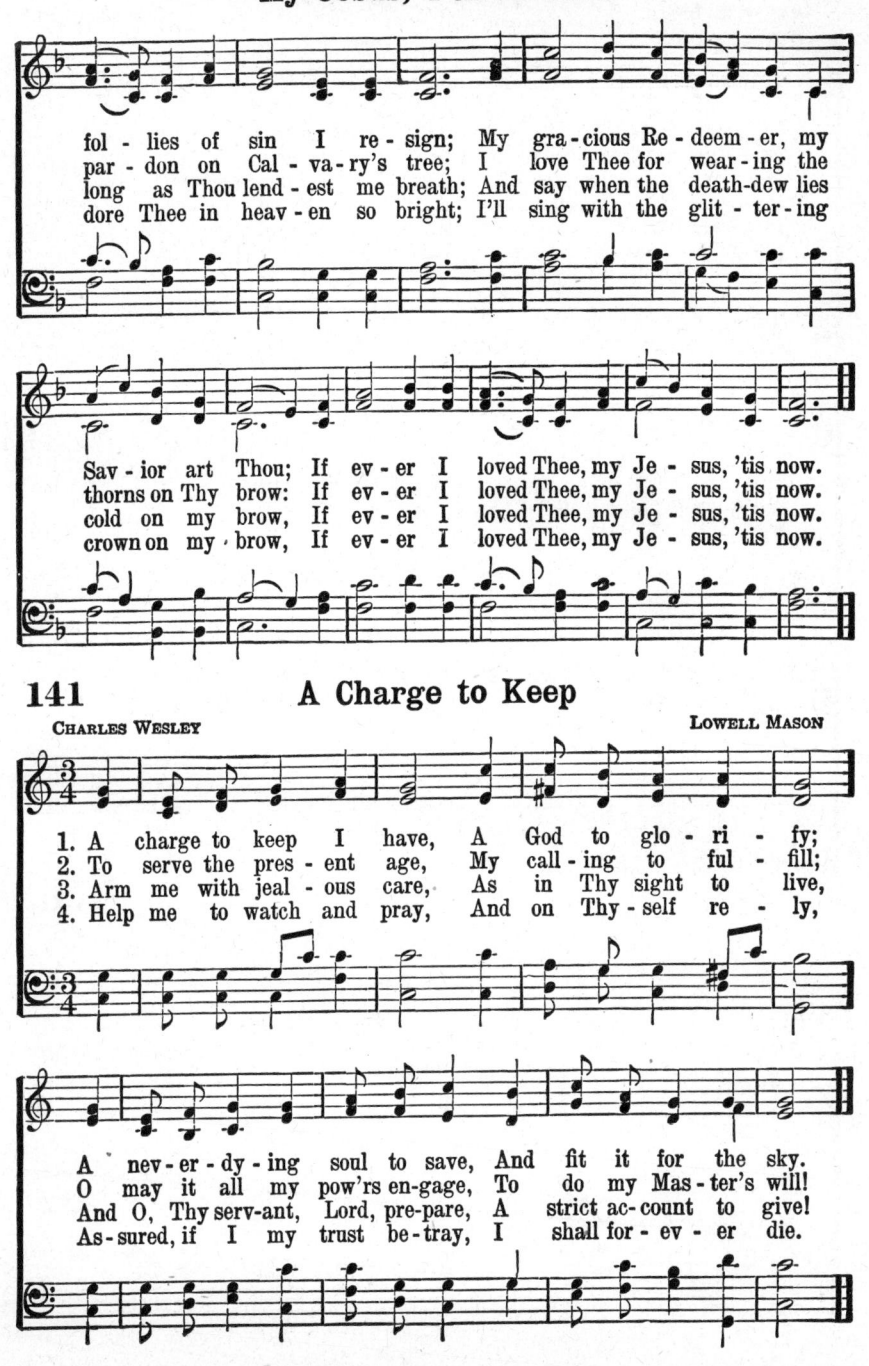

fol - lies of sin I re - sign; My gra - cious Re - deem - er, my
par - don on Cal - va - ry's tree; I love Thee for wear - ing the
long as Thou lend - est me breath; And say when the death-dew lies
dore Thee in heav - en so bright; I'll sing with the glit - ter - ing

Sav - ior art Thou; If ev - er I loved Thee, my Je - sus, 'tis now.
thorns on Thy brow: If ev - er I loved Thee, my Je - sus, 'tis now.
cold on my brow, If ev - er I loved Thee, my Je - sus, 'tis now.
crown on my brow, If ev - er I loved Thee, my Je - sus, 'tis now.

## 141    A Charge to Keep

CHARLES WESLEY     LOWELL MASON

1. A charge to keep I have, A God to glo - ri - fy;
2. To serve the pres - ent age, My call - ing to ful - fill;
3. Arm me with jeal - ous care, As in Thy sight to live,
4. Help me to watch and pray, And on Thy - self re - ly,

A nev - er - dy - ing soul to save, And fit it for the sky.
O may it all my pow'rs en - gage, To do my Mas - ter's will!
And O, Thy serv - ant, Lord, pre - pare, A strict ac - count to give!
As - sured, if I my trust be - tray, I shall for - ev - er die.

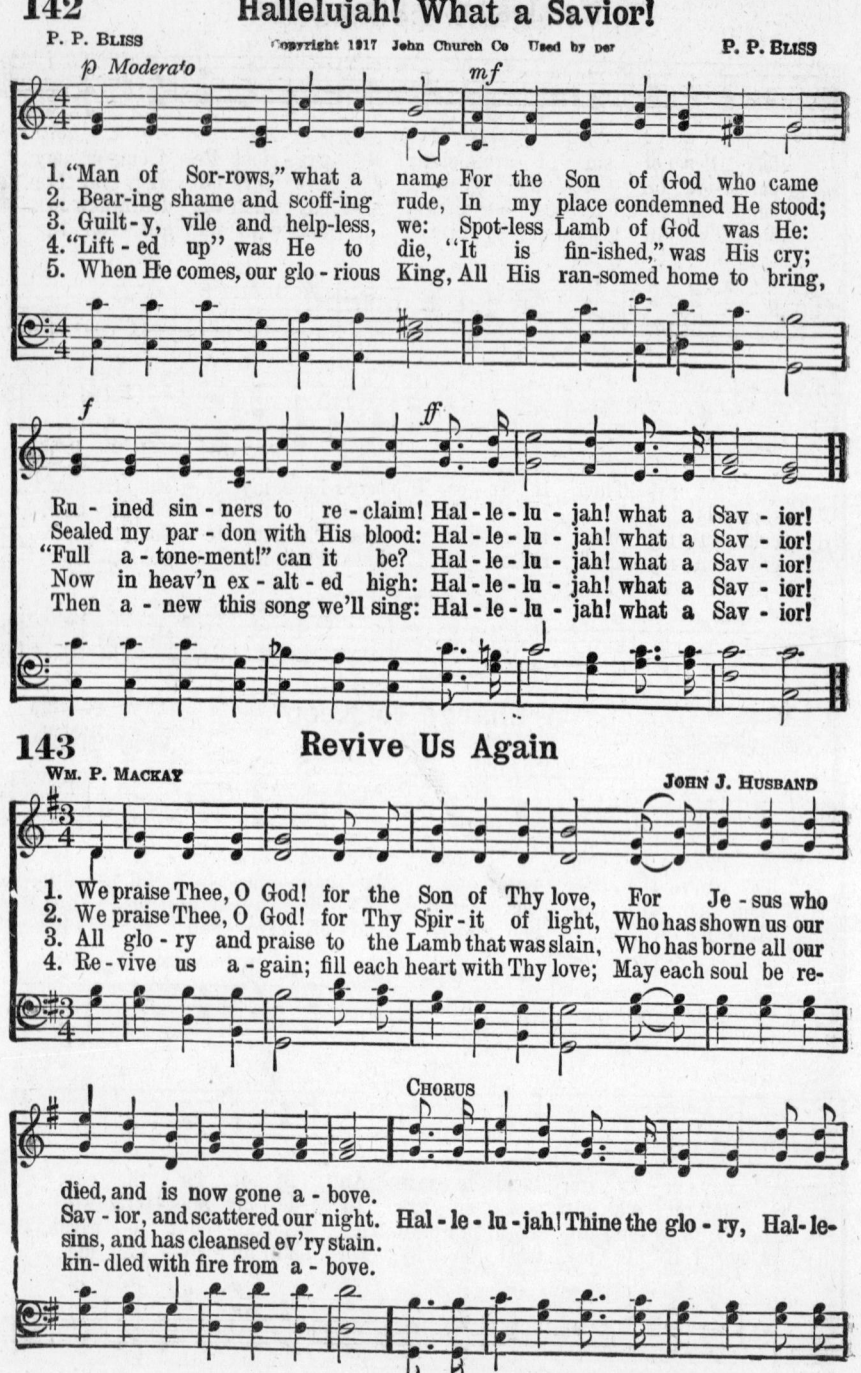

## 142 Hallelujah! What a Savior!

P. P. BLISS

Copyright 1917 John Church Co   Used by per

P. P. BLISS

*p* Moderato

1. "Man of Sor-rows," what a name For the Son of God who came
2. Bear-ing shame and scoff-ing rude, In my place condemned He stood;
3. Guilt-y, vile and help-less, we: Spot-less Lamb of God was He:
4. "Lift-ed up" was He to die, "It is fin-ished," was His cry;
5. When He comes, our glo-rious King, All His ran-somed home to bring,

Ru - ined sin - ners to re - claim! Hal - le - lu - jah! what a Sav - ior!
Sealed my par - don with His blood: Hal - le - lu - jah! what a Sav - ior!
"Full a - tone-ment!" can it be? Hal - le - lu - jah! what a Sav - ior!
Now in heav'n ex - alt - ed high: Hal - le - lu - jah! what a Sav - ior!
Then a - new this song we'll sing: Hal - le - lu - jah! what a Sav - ior!

## 143 Revive Us Again

WM. P. MACKAY

JOHN J. HUSBAND

1. We praise Thee, O God! for the Son of Thy love, For Je - sus who
2. We praise Thee, O God! for Thy Spir - it of light, Who has shown us our
3. All glo - ry and praise to the Lamb that was slain, Who has borne all our
4. Re - vive us a - gain; fill each heart with Thy love; May each soul be re-

CHORUS

died, and is now gone a - bove.
Sav - ior, and scattered our night.   Hal - le - lu - jah! Thine the glo - ry, Hal - le -
sins, and has cleansed ev'ry stain.
kin - dled with fire from a - bove.

# Revive Us Again

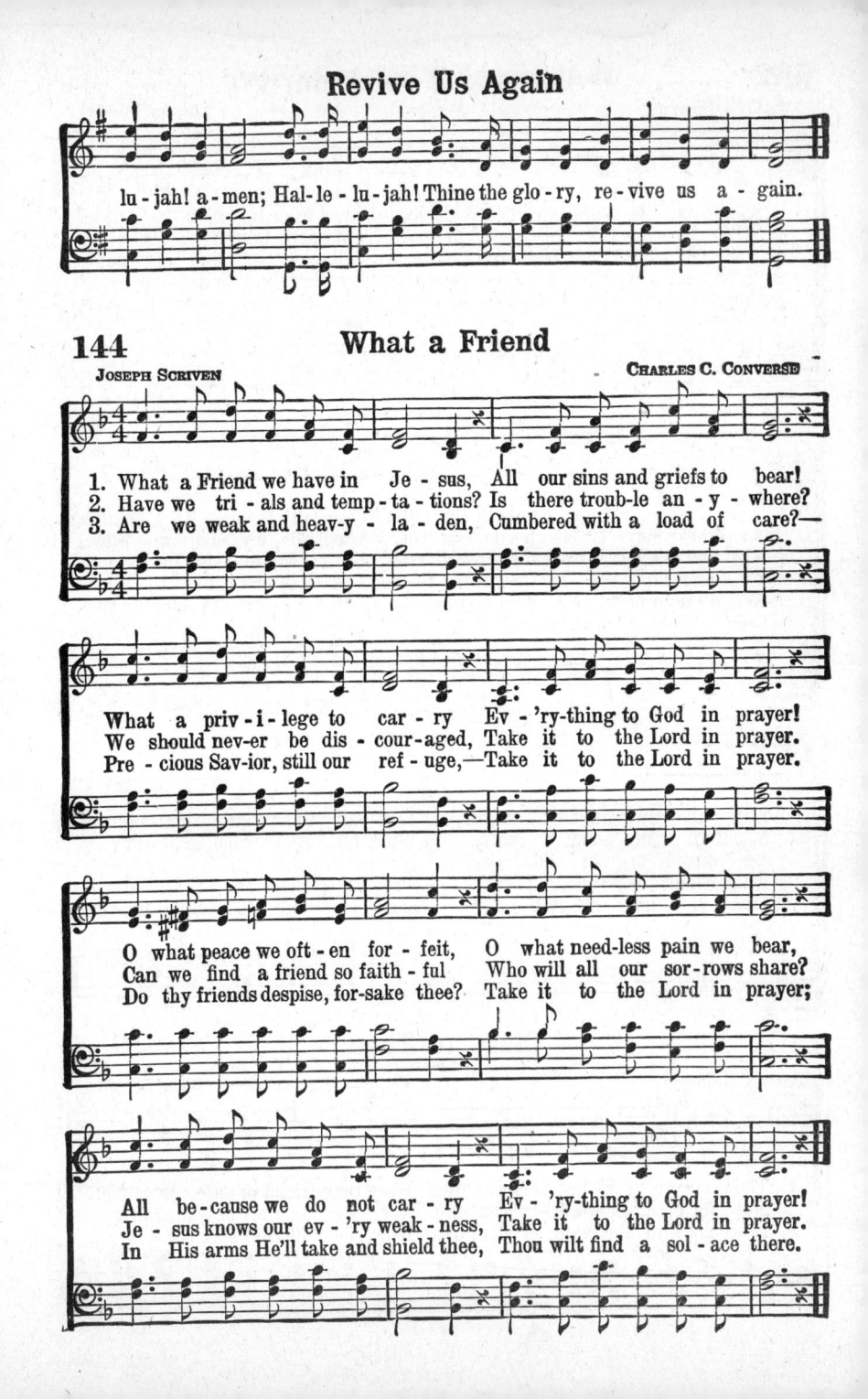

lu-jah! a-men; Hal-le-lu-jah! Thine the glo-ry, re-vive us a-gain.

## 144. What a Friend

JOSEPH SCRIVEN  
CHARLES C. CONVERSE

1. What a Friend we have in Je-sus, All our sins and griefs to bear!
2. Have we tri-als and temp-ta-tions? Is there troub-le an-y-where?
3. Are we weak and heav-y-la-den, Cumbered with a load of care?—

What a priv-i-lege to car-ry Ev-'ry-thing to God in prayer!
We should nev-er be dis-cour-aged, Take it to the Lord in prayer.
Pre-cious Sav-ior, still our ref-uge,—Take it to the Lord in prayer.

O what peace we oft-en for-feit, O what need-less pain we bear,
Can we find a friend so faith-ful, Who will all our sor-rows share?
Do thy friends despise, for-sake thee? Take it to the Lord in prayer;

All be-cause we do not car-ry Ev-'ry-thing to God in prayer!
Je-sus knows our ev-'ry weak-ness, Take it to the Lord in prayer.
In His arms He'll take and shield thee, Thou wilt find a sol-ace there.

## 145. There is a Fountain

*William Cowper* — *Lowell Mason*

1. There is a foun-tain filled with blood Drawn from Im-man-uel's veins;
2. The dy-ing thief re-joiced to see That foun-tain in his day;
3. Dear dy-ing Lamb, Thy pre-cious blood Shall nev-er lose its pow'r,
4. E'er since, by faith, I saw the stream Thy flow-ing wounds sup-ply,
5. Then in a no-bler, sweet-er song, I'll sing Thy pow'r to save,

*D.S.*—And sin-ners, plunged be-neath that flood, Lose all their guilt-y stains.
*D.S.*—And there may I, though vile as he, Wash all my sins a-way.
*D.S.*—Till all the ran-somed church of God Be saved, to sin no more.
*D.S.*—Re-deem-ing love has been my theme, And shall be till I die.
*D.S.*—When this poor lisp-ing, stamm'ring tongue Lies si-lent in the grave.

Lose all their guilt-y stains, Lose all their guilt-y stains;
Wash all my sins a-way, Wash all my sins a-way;
Be saved, to sin no more, Be saved, to sin no more;
And shall be till I die, And shall be till I die;
Lies si-lent in the grave, Lies si-lent in the grave;

## 146. Close to Thee

*Fanny J. Crosby* — *Silas J. Vail*

1. Thou, my ev-er-last-ing por-tion, More than friend or life to me;
2. Not for ease or world-ly pleas-ure, Nor for fame my prayer shall be;
3. Lead me thro' the vale of shad-ows, Bear me o'er life's fit-ful sea;

## Close to Thee

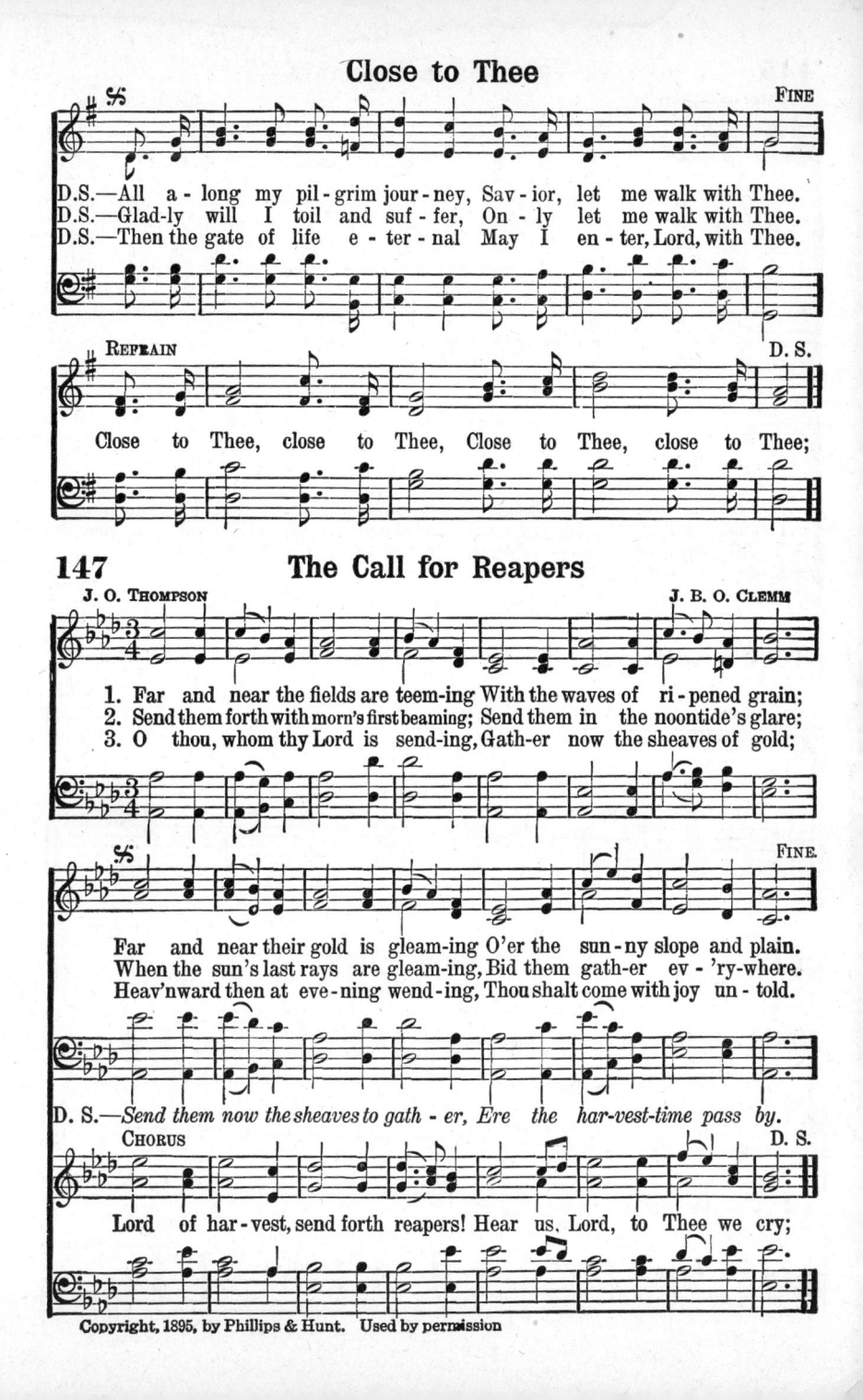

D.S.—All a-long my pil-grim jour-ney, Sav-ior, let me walk with Thee.
D.S.—Glad-ly will I toil and suf-fer, On-ly let me walk with Thee.
D.S.—Then the gate of life e-ter-nal May I en-ter, Lord, with Thee.

REFRAIN

Close to Thee, close to Thee, Close to Thee, close to Thee;

---

## 147. The Call for Reapers

J. O. THOMPSON  J. B. O. CLEMM

1. Far and near the fields are teem-ing With the waves of ri-pened grain;
2. Send them forth with morn's first beaming; Send them in the noontide's glare;
3. O thou, whom thy Lord is send-ing, Gath-er now the sheaves of gold;

Far and near their gold is gleam-ing O'er the sun-ny slope and plain.
When the sun's last rays are gleam-ing, Bid them gath-er ev-'ry-where.
Heav'nward then at eve-ning wend-ing, Thou shalt come with joy un-told.

D. S.—Send them now the sheaves to gath-er, Ere the har-vest-time pass by.

CHORUS

Lord of har-vest, send forth reapers! Hear us, Lord, to Thee we cry;

Copyright, 1895, by Phillips & Hunt. Used by permission.

## 148  Fill Me Now

E. R. Stokes, D. D.  
Jno. R. Sweney

1. Hover o'er me, Holy Spirit, Bathe my trembling heart and brow;
2. Thou canst fill me, gracious Spirit, Though I cannot tell Thee how;
3. I am weakness, full of weakness, At Thy sacred feet I bow;
4. Cleanse and comfort, bless and save me, Bathe, O bathe my heart and brow;

Fill me with Thy hallowed presence, Come, O come and fill me now.
But I need Thee, greatly need Thee, Come, O come and fill me now.
Blest, divine, eternal Spirit, Fill with pow'r, and fill me now.
Thou art comforting and saving, Thou art sweetly filling now.

D.S.—Fill me with Thy hallowed presence, Come, O come and fill me now.

**Chorus**

Fill me now, fill me now, Jesus, come and fill me now;

Copyright, 1907, by Jno. R. Sweney. Renewal

## 149  O Happy Day

Philip Doddridge  
E. F. Rimbault

1. O happy day that fixed my choice On Thee, my Savior and my God!
   Well may this glowing heart rejoice, And tell its raptures all abroad.
2. O happy bond, that seals my vows To Him who merits all my love!
   Let cheerful anthems fill His house, While to that sacred shrine I move.
3. 'Tis done: the great transaction's done; I am my Lord's, and He is mine;
   He drew me, and I followed on, Charmed to confess the voice divine.
4. Now rest, my long-divided heart; Fixed on this blissful centre, rest;
   Nor ever from my Lord depart, With Him of ev'ry good possessed.

# O Happy Day

Hap-py day, hap-py day, When Je-sus washed my sins a-way!

He taught me how to watch and pray, And live re-joic-ing ev-'ry day;

## 150 Only Trust Him

J. H. S.     J. H. Stockton

1. Come, ev-'ry soul by sin op-pressed, There's mer-cy with the Lord,
2. For Je-sus shed His pre-cious blood Rich bless-ings to be-stow;
3. Yes, Je-sus is the Truth, the Way, That leads you in-to rest:
4. Come, then, and join this ho-ly band, And on to glo-ry go,

And He will sure-ly give you rest By trust-ing in His word.
Plunge now in-to the crim-son flood That wash-es white as snow.
Be-lieve in Him with-out de-lay, And you are ful-ly blest.
To dwell in that ce-les-tial land Where joys im-mor-tal flow.

**Chorus**

On-ly trust Him, on-ly trust Him, On-ly trust Him now;
He will save you, He will save you, He will (*Omit.....*) save you now.

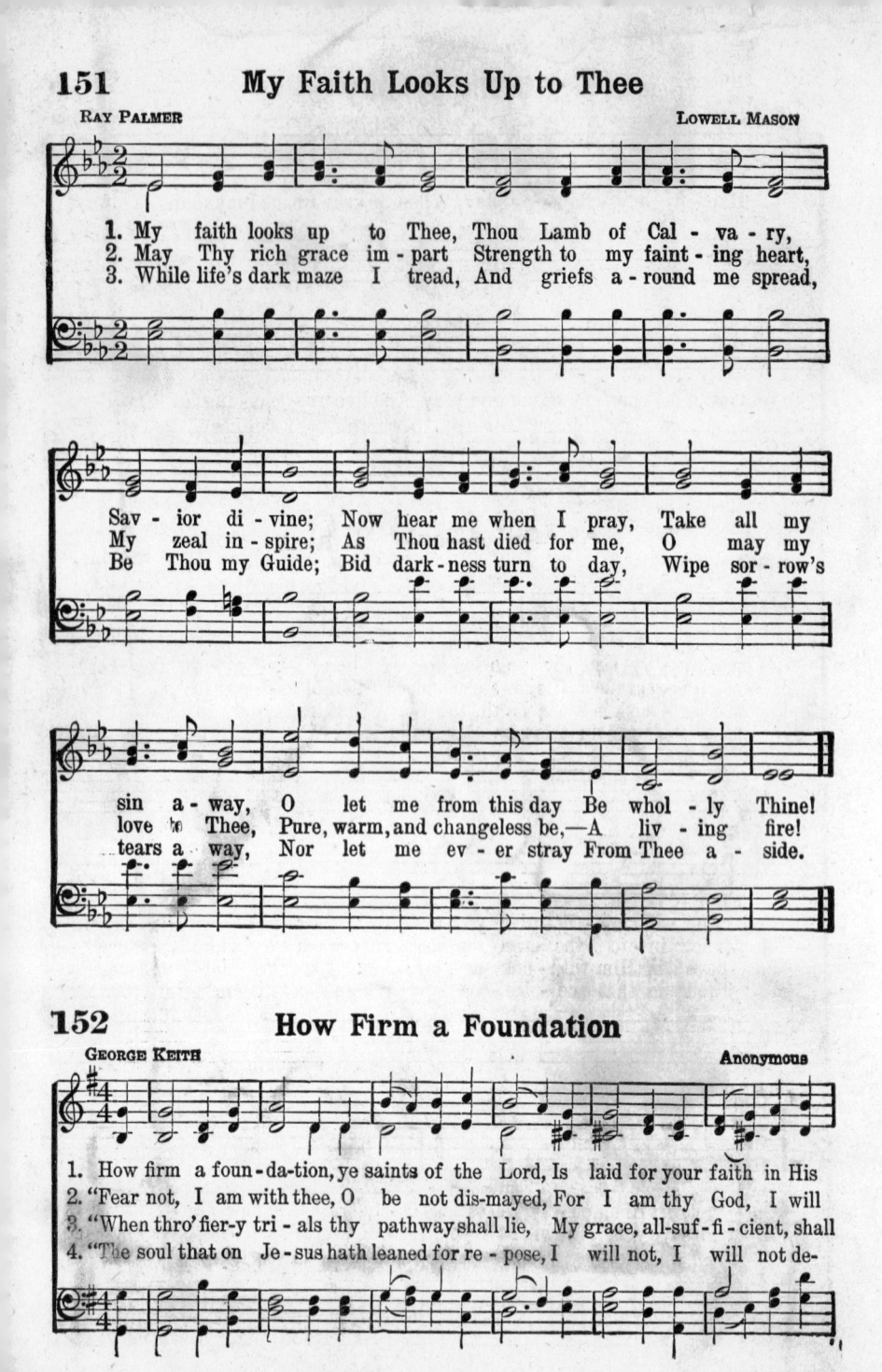

## 151  My Faith Looks Up to Thee

RAY PALMER  LOWELL MASON

1. My faith looks up to Thee, Thou Lamb of Cal-va-ry,
Sav-ior di-vine; Now hear me when I pray, Take all my
sin a-way, O let me from this day Be whol-ly Thine!

2. May Thy rich grace im-part Strength to my faint-ing heart,
My zeal in-spire; As Thou hast died for me, O may my
love to Thee, Pure, warm, and changeless be,—A liv-ing fire!

3. While life's dark maze I tread, And griefs a-round me spread,
Be Thou my Guide; Bid dark-ness turn to day, Wipe sor-row's
tears a-way, Nor let me ev-er stray From Thee a-side.

## 152  How Firm a Foundation

GEORGE KEITH  Anonymous

1. How firm a foun-da-tion, ye saints of the Lord, Is laid for your faith in His
2. "Fear not, I am with thee, O be not dis-mayed, For I am thy God, I will
3. "When thro' fier-y tri-als thy pathway shall lie, My grace, all-suf-fi-cient, shall
4. "The soul that on Je-sus hath leaned for re-pose, I will not, I will not de-

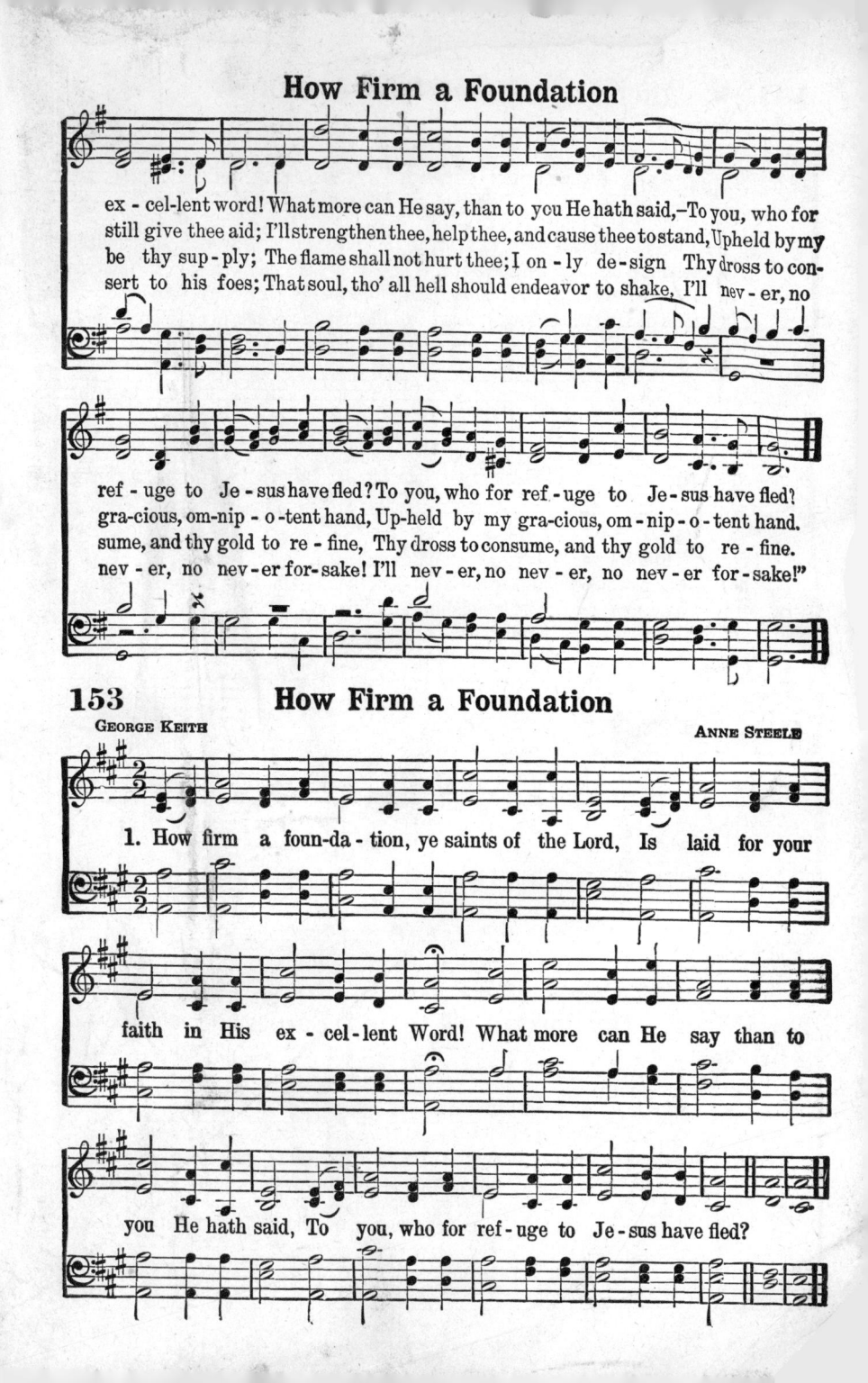

## How Firm a Foundation

ex - cel-lent word! What more can He say, than to you He hath said,—To you, who for
still give thee aid; I'll strengthen thee, help thee, and cause thee to stand, Upheld by my
be thy sup - ply; The flame shall not hurt thee; I on - ly de - sign Thy dross to con-
sert to his foes; That soul, tho' all hell should endeavor to shake, I'll nev - er, no

ref - uge to Je - sus have fled? To you, who for ref - uge to Je - sus have fled?
gra - cious, om - nip - o - tent hand, Up - held by my gra - cious, om - nip - o - tent hand.
sume, and thy gold to re - fine, Thy dross to consume, and thy gold to re - fine.
nev - er, no nev - er for - sake! I'll nev - er, no nev - er, no nev - er for - sake!"

### 153 How Firm a Foundation

GEORGE KEITH

ANNE STEELE

1. How firm a foun - da - tion, ye saints of the Lord, Is laid for your
faith in His ex - cel - lent Word! What more can He say than to
you He hath said, To you, who for ref - uge to Je - sus have fled?

## 154. There is a Name I Love to Hear

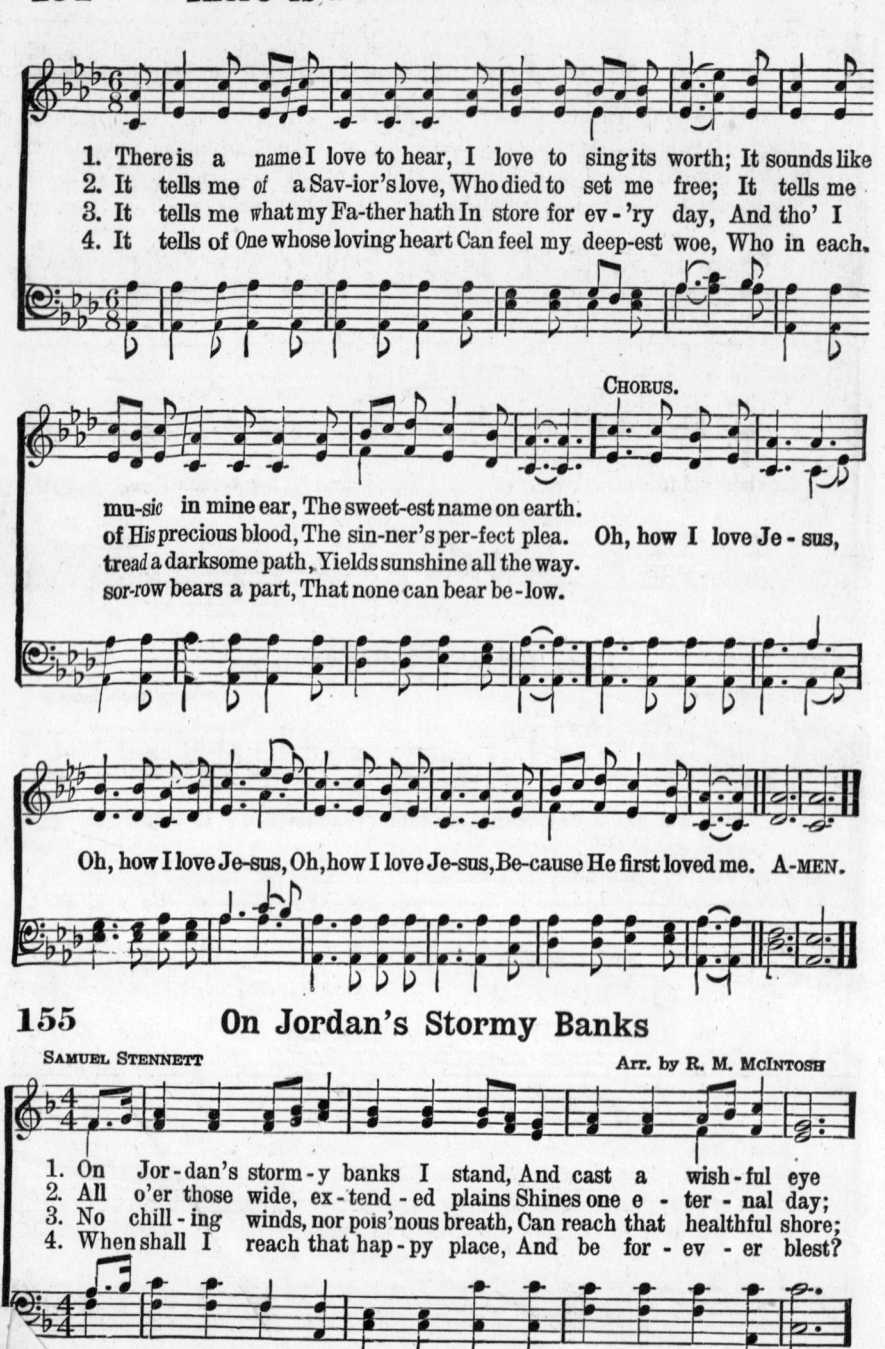

1. There is a name I love to hear, I love to sing its worth; It sounds like mu-sic in mine ear, The sweet-est name on earth.
2. It tells me of a Sav-ior's love, Who died to set me free; It tells me of His precious blood, The sin-ner's per-fect plea.
3. It tells me what my Fa-ther hath In store for ev-'ry day, And tho' I tread a darksome path, Yields sunshine all the way.
4. It tells of One whose loving heart Can feel my deep-est woe, Who in each sor-row bears a part, That none can bear be-low.

CHORUS.

Oh, how I love Je-sus, Oh, how I love Je-sus, Oh, how I love Je-sus, Be-cause He first loved me. A-MEN.

## 155. On Jordan's Stormy Banks

SAMUEL STENNETT     Arr. by R. M. MCINTOSH

1. On Jor-dan's storm-y banks I stand, And cast a wish-ful eye
2. All o'er those wide, ex-tend-ed plains Shines one e-ter-nal day;
3. No chill-ing winds, nor pois'nous breath, Can reach that healthful shore;
4. When shall I reach that hap-py place, And be for-ev-er blest?

## On Jordan's Stormy Banks

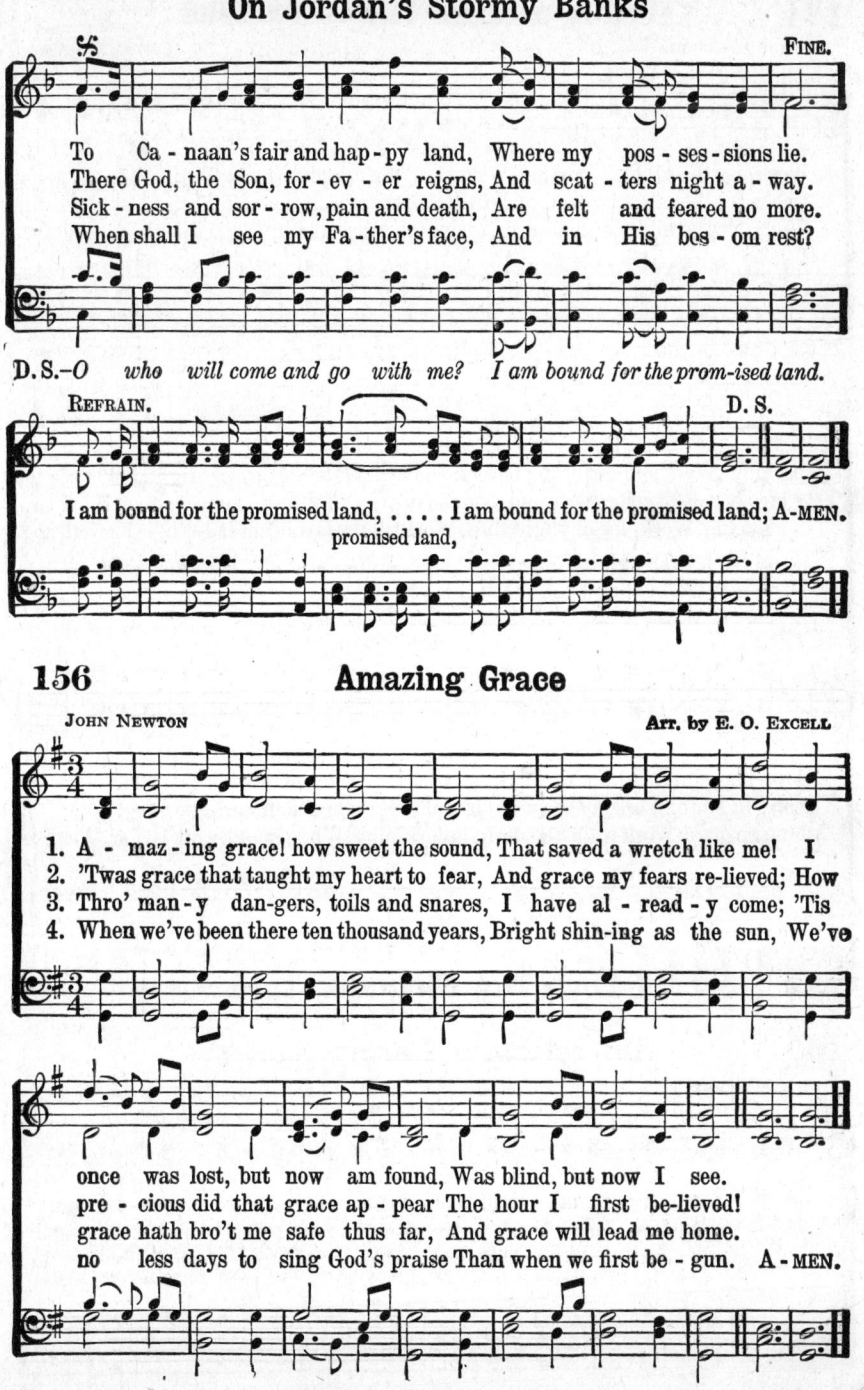

To Canaan's fair and happy land, Where my possessions lie.
There God, the Son, forever reigns, And scatters night away.
Sickness and sorrow, pain and death, Are felt and feared no more.
When shall I see my Father's face, And in His bosom rest?

D. S.—O who will come and go with me? I am bound for the promised land.

**Refrain.**
I am bound for the promised land, .... I am bound for the promised land; A-MEN.

## 156  Amazing Grace

JOHN NEWTON  
Arr. by E. O. EXCELL

1. Amazing grace! how sweet the sound, That saved a wretch like me! I
2. 'Twas grace that taught my heart to fear, And grace my fears relieved; How
3. Thro' many dangers, toils and snares, I have already come; 'Tis
4. When we've been there ten thousand years, Bright shining as the sun, We've

once was lost, but now am found, Was blind, but now I see.
precious did that grace appear The hour I first believed!
grace hath bro't me safe thus far, And grace will lead me home.
no less days to sing God's praise Than when we first begun. A-MEN.

## 157. Work, For the Night is Coming

ANNIE L. COGHILL  
LOWELL MASON

1. Work, for the night is coming, Work thro' the morning hours; Work while the dew is sparkling, Work 'mid springing flow'rs; Work when the day grows brighter, Work in the glowing sun; Work, for the night is coming, When man's work is done.

2. Work, for the night is coming, Work thro' the sunny noon; Fill brightest hours with labor, Rest comes sure and soon. Give ev'ry flying minute Something to keep in store: Work, for the night is coming, When man works no more.

3. Work, for the night is coming, Under the sunset skies; While their bright tints are glowing, Work, for daylight flies. Work till the last beam fadeth, Fadeth to shine no more; Work while the night is dark'ning, When man's work is o'er. A-MEN.

## 158. I Love Thy Kingdom, Lord

TIMOTHY DWIGHT  
AARON WILLIAMS, Coll.

1. I love Thy kingdom, Lord, The house of Thine abode,
2. I love Thy Church, O God! Her walls before Thee stand,
3. For her my tears shall fall; For her my prayers ascend;
4. Beyond my highest joy I prize her heav'nly ways,
5. Sure as Thy truth shall last, To Zion shall be giv'n

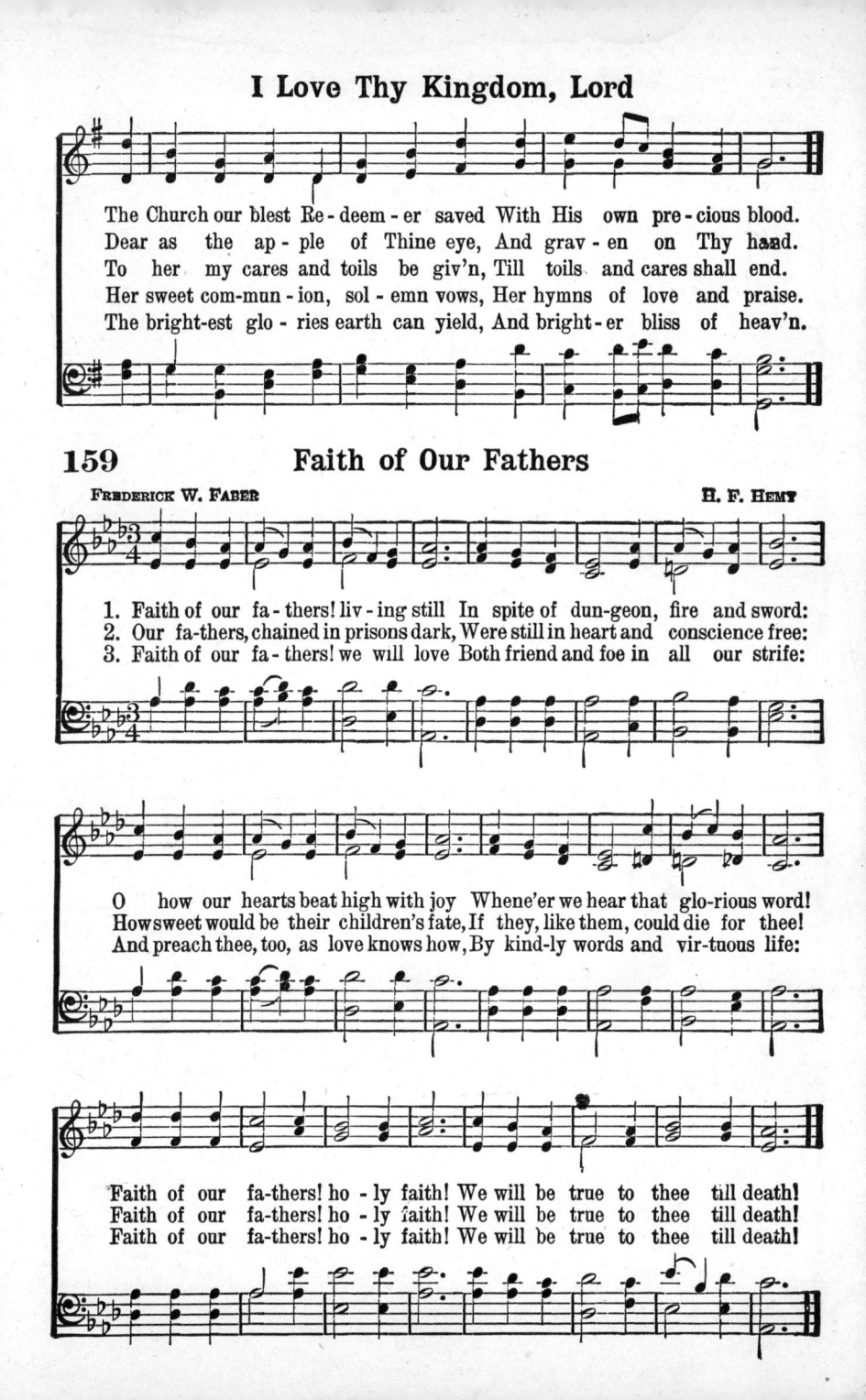

## I Love Thy Kingdom, Lord

The Church our blest Re-deem-er saved With His own pre-cious blood.
Dear as the ap-ple of Thine eye, And grav-en on Thy hand.
To her my cares and toils be giv'n, Till toils and cares shall end.
Her sweet com-mun-ion, sol-emn vows, Her hymns of love and praise.
The bright-est glo-ries earth can yield, And bright-er bliss of heav'n.

## 159    Faith of Our Fathers

FREDERICK W. FABER     H. F. HEMY

1. Faith of our fa-thers! liv-ing still In spite of dun-geon, fire and sword:
2. Our fa-thers, chained in prisons dark, Were still in heart and conscience free:
3. Faith of our fa-thers! we will love Both friend and foe in all our strife:

O how our hearts beat high with joy Whene'er we hear that glo-rious word!
How sweet would be their children's fate, If they, like them, could die for thee!
And preach thee, too, as love knows how, By kind-ly words and vir-tuous life:

Faith of our fa-thers! ho-ly faith! We will be true to thee till death!
Faith of our fa-thers! ho-ly faith! We will be true to thee till death!
Faith of our fa-thers! ho-ly faith! We will be true to thee till death!

## 160. Wonderful Words of Life

*P. P. B.*              *P. P. Bliss*

1. Sing them over again to me, Wonderful words of Life;
   Let me more of their beauty see, Wonderful words of Life.
   Words of life and beauty, Teach me faith and duty:

2. Christ, the blessed One, gives to all, Wonderful words of Life;
   Sinner, list to the loving call, Wonderful words of Life.
   All so freely given, Wooing us to Heaven:

3. Sweetly echo the gospel call, Wonderful words of Life;
   Offer pardon and peace to all, Wonderful words of Life.
   Jesus, only Savior, Sanctify forever:

**Refrain**
Beautiful words, wonderful words, Wonderful words of Life.

## 161. Jesus Calls Us

*Mrs. Cecil F. Alexander*              *William H. Jude*

1. Jesus calls us; o'er the tumult Of our life's wild, restless sea,
2. Jesus calls us from the worship Of the vain world's golden store,
3. In our joys and in our sorrows, Days of toil and hours of ease,
4. Jesus calls us: by Thy mercies, Savior, may we hear Thy call,

## Jesus Calls Us

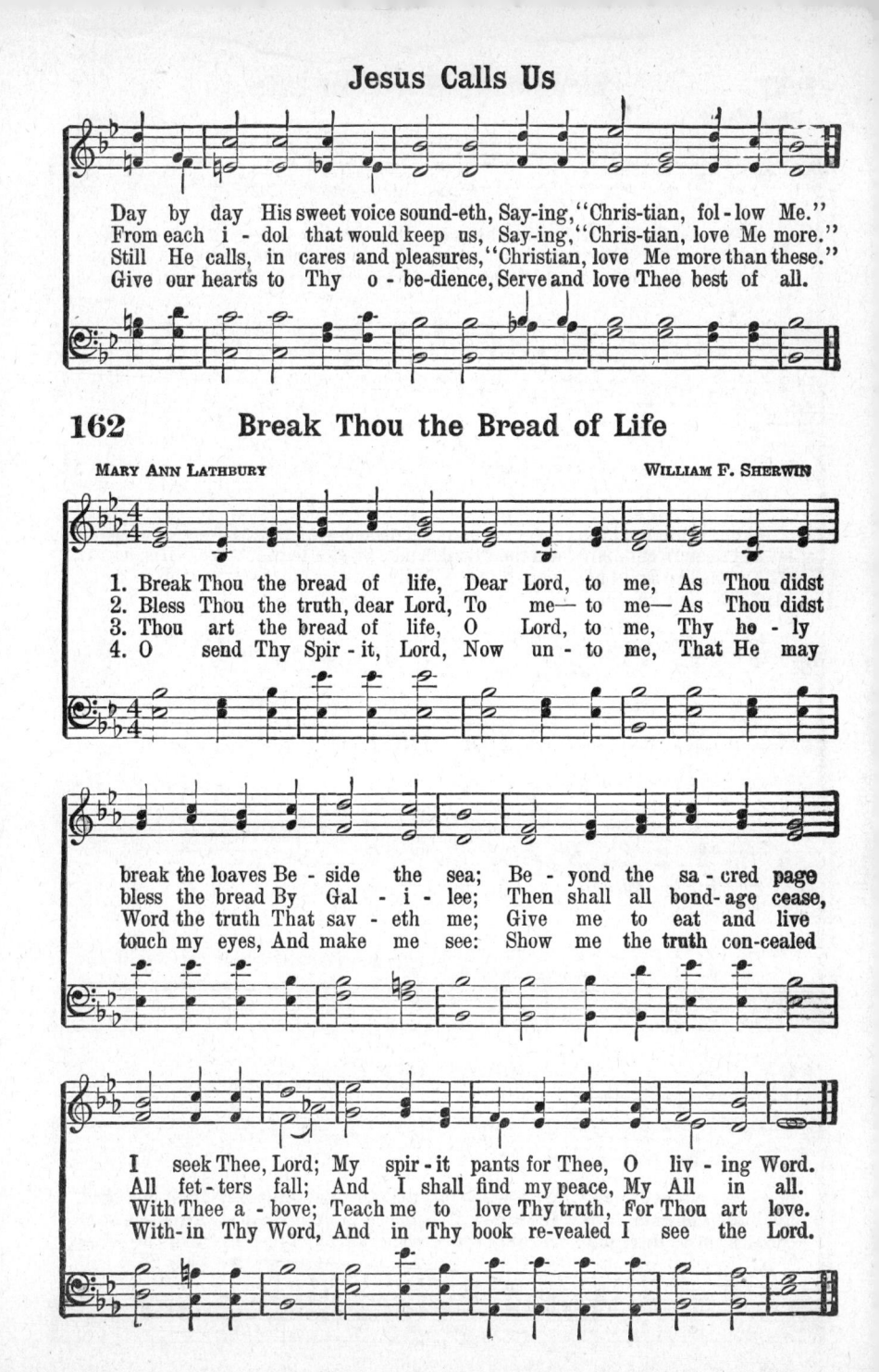

Day by day His sweet voice sound-eth, Say-ing, "Chris-tian, fol-low Me."
From each i-dol that would keep us, Say-ing, "Chris-tian, love Me more."
Still He calls, in cares and pleasures, "Christian, love Me more than these."
Give our hearts to Thy o-be-dience, Serve and love Thee best of all.

## 162  Break Thou the Bread of Life

MARY ANN LATHBURY     WILLIAM F. SHERWIN

1. Break Thou the bread of life, Dear Lord, to me, As Thou didst break the loaves Be-side the sea; Be-yond the sa-cred page I seek Thee, Lord; My spir-it pants for Thee, O liv-ing Word.
2. Bless Thou the truth, dear Lord, To me— to me— As Thou didst bless the bread By Gal-i-lee; Then shall all bond-age cease, All fet-ters fall; And I shall find my peace, My All in all.
3. Thou art the bread of life, O Lord, to me, Thy ho-ly Word the truth That sav-eth me; Give me to eat and live With Thee a-bove; Teach me to love Thy truth, for Thou art love.
4. O send Thy Spir-it, Lord, Now un-to me, That He may touch my eyes, And make me see: Show me the truth con-cealed With-in Thy Word, And in Thy book re-vealed I see the Lord.

## 163 Jesus Shall Reign

ISAAC WATTS
JOHN HATTON

1. Je-sus shall reign wher-e'er the sun Does his suc-ces-sive jour-neys run;
2. From north to south the prin-ces meet To pay their hom-age at His feet;
3. To Him shall end-less prayer be made, And end-less prais-es crown His head;
4. Peo-ple and realms of ev-'ry tongue Dwell on His love with sweetest song,

His kingdom spread from shore to shore, Till moons shall wax and wane no more.
While western em-pires own their Lord, And sav-age tribes at-tend His word.
His name like sweet per-fume shall rise With ev-'ry morn-ing sac-ri-fice.
And in-fant voi-ces shall pro-claim Their earth-ly bless-ings on His name.

## 164 O Zion, Haste

MARY A. THOMSON
JAMES WALCH

1. O Zi-on, haste, thy mis-sion high ful-fill-ing, To tell to all the
2. Be-hold how man-y thousands still are ly-ing, Bound in the dark-some
3. Pro-claim to ev-'ry peo-ple, tongue and na-tion That God in Whom they
4. Give of thy sons to bear the mes-sage glo-rious; Give of thy wealth to

world that God is Light; That He who made all na-tions is not will-ing
pris-on-house of sin, With none to tell them of the Sav-ior's dy-ing,
live and move is love: Tell how He stooped to save His lost cre-a-tion,
speed them on their way; Pour out thy soul for them in prayer vic-to-rious;

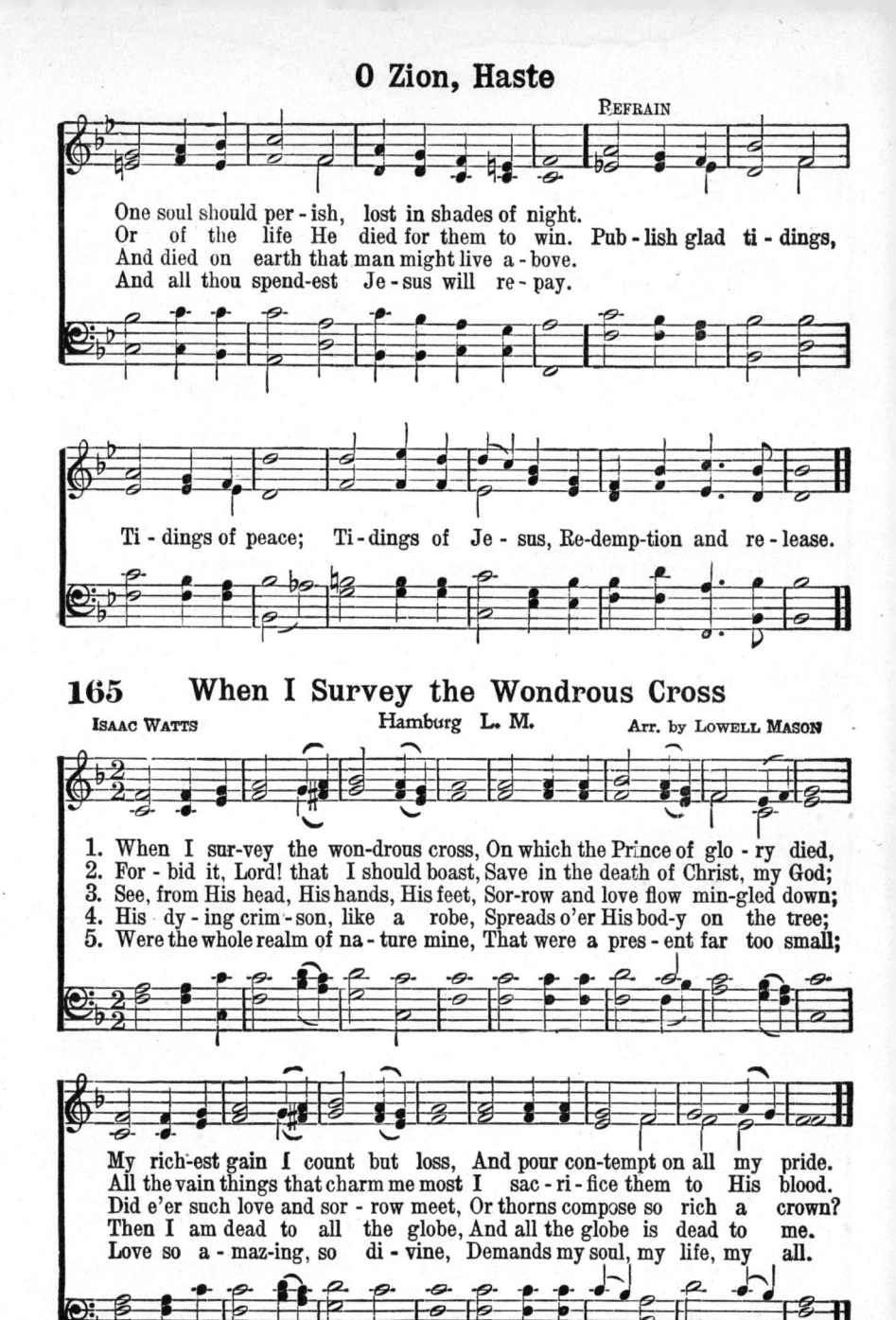

## O Zion, Haste

One soul should per-ish, lost in shades of night.
Or of the life He died for them to win. Pub-lish glad ti-dings,
And died on earth that man might live a-bove.
And all thou spend-est Je-sus will re-pay.

REFRAIN

Ti-dings of peace; Ti-dings of Je-sus, Re-demp-tion and re-lease.

## 165  When I Survey the Wondrous Cross

ISAAC WATTS    Hamburg L. M.    Arr. by LOWELL MASON

1. When I sur-vey the won-drous cross, On which the Prince of glo-ry died,
2. For-bid it, Lord! that I should boast, Save in the death of Christ, my God;
3. See, from His head, His hands, His feet, Sor-row and love flow min-gled down;
4. His dy-ing crim-son, like a robe, Spreads o'er His bod-y on the tree;
5. Were the whole realm of na-ture mine, That were a pres-ent far too small;

My rich-est gain I count but loss, And pour con-tempt on all my pride.
All the vain things that charm me most I sac-ri-fice them to His blood.
Did e'er such love and sor-row meet, Or thorns compose so rich a crown?
Then I am dead to all the globe, And all the globe is dead to me.
Love so a-maz-ing, so di-vine, Demands my soul, my life, my all.

## 166 Rock of Ages

Augustus M. Toplady  
Thomas Hastings

1. Rock of A-ges, cleft for me, Let me hide my-self in Thee;
2. Could my tears for-ev-er flow, Could my zeal no lan-guor know,
3. While I draw this fleet-ing breath, When my eyes shall close in death,

Let the wa-ter and the blood, From Thy wound-ed side which flowed,
These for sin could not a-tone; Thou must save, and Thou a-lone:
When I rise to worlds un-known, And be-hold Thee on Thy throne,

Be of sin the doub-le cure, Save from wrath and make me pure.
In my hand no price I bring, Sim-ply to Thy cross I cling.
Rock of A-ges, cleft for me, Let me hide my-self in Thee.

## 167 Nearer, My God, to Thee

Sarah F. Adams  
Arr. by Lowell Mason

1. Near-er, my God, to Thee, Near-er to Thee! E'en though it
2. Though like the wan-der-er, The sun gone down, Dark-ness be
3. There let the way ap-pear, Steps un-to Heav'n: All that Thou
4. Then, with my wak-ing tho'ts Bright with Thy praise, Out of my
5. Or if on joy-ful wing, Cleav-ing the sky, Sun, moon, and

## Nearer, My God, to Thee

be a cross That rais-eth me; Still all my song shall be,
o - ver me, My rest a stone; Yet in my dreams I'd be
send-est me, In mer-cy giv'n: An - gels to beck-on me,
sto - ny griefs Beth-el I'll raise; So by my woes to be
stars for-got, Up - wards I'll fly, Still all my song shall be,

Near-er, my God, to Thee, Near-er, my God, to Thee, Near-er to Thee!

## 168 Jesus, Lover of My Soul

CHARLES WESLEY  
S. B. MARSH  
FINE

1. { Je - sus, Lov - er of my soul, Let me to Thy bos - om fly,
   { While the near-er wa-ters roll, While the tem-pest still is high!
2. { Oth - er ref - uge have I none; Hangs my help-less soul on Thee:
   { Leave, ah, leave me not a - lone, Still sup-port and com - fort me!
3. { Thou, O Christ, art all I want; More than all in Thee I find;
   { Raise the fall - en, cheer the faint, Heal the sick, and lead the blind.
4. { Plenteous grace with Thee is found, Grace to cov - er all my sin;
   { Let the heal-ing streams a-bound, Make and keep me pure with - in.

D.C.—Safe in - to the ha - ven guide, O re-ceive my soul at last!
D.C.—Cov - er my de-fense-less head With the shad-ow of Thy wing.
D.C.—False and full of sin I am, Thou art full of truth and grace.
D.C.—Spring Thou up with - in my heart, Rise to all e - ter - ni - ty.

D.C.

Hide me, O my Sav - ior, hide, Till the storm of life is past;
All my trust on Thee is stayed, All my help from Thee I bring;
Just and ho - ly is Thy name, I am all un-right-eous - ness;
Thou of life the foun - tain art; Free-ly let me take of Thee;

## 169 Blest Be the Tie

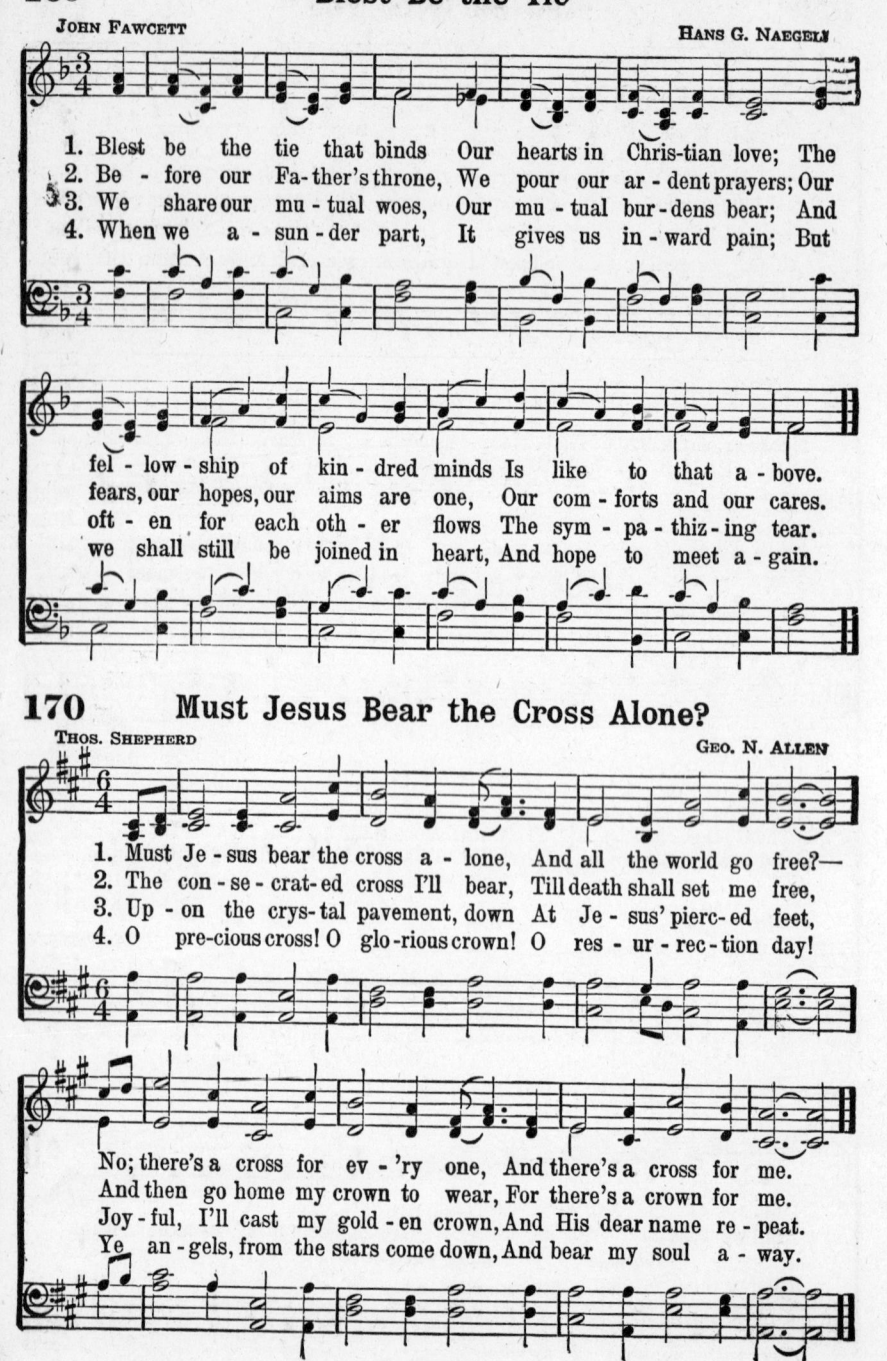

JOHN FAWCETT  
HANS G. NAEGELI

1. Blest be the tie that binds Our hearts in Christian love; The fellowship of kindred minds Is like to that above.
2. Before our Father's throne, We pour our ardent prayers; Our fears, our hopes, our aims are one, Our comforts and our cares.
3. We share our mutual woes, Our mutual burdens bear; And often for each other flows The sympathizing tear.
4. When we asunder part, It gives us inward pain; But we shall still be joined in heart, And hope to meet again.

## 170 Must Jesus Bear the Cross Alone?

THOS. SHEPHERD  
GEO. N. ALLEN

1. Must Jesus bear the cross alone, And all the world go free?— No; there's a cross for ev-'ry one, And there's a cross for me.
2. The consecrated cross I'll bear, Till death shall set me free, And then go home my crown to wear, For there's a crown for me.
3. Upon the crystal pavement, down At Jesus' pierced feet, Joyful, I'll cast my golden crown, And His dear name repeat.
4. O precious cross! O glorious crown! O resurrection day! Ye angels, from the stars come down, And bear my soul away.

## 171. God Be With You

J. E. Rankin  
W. G. Tomer

1. God be with you till we meet a-gain; By His counsels guide, uphold you,
2. God be with you till we meet a-gain; 'Neath His wings protecting hide you,
3. God be with you till we meet a-gain; When life's perils thick confound you,
4. God be with you till we meet a-gain; Keep love's banner floating o'er you;

With His sheep se-cure-ly fold you; God be with you till we meet a-gain.
Dai-ly man-na still pro-vide you; God be with you till we meet a-gain.
Put His arms un-fail-ing round you; God be with you till we meet a-gain.
Smite death's threat'ning wave before you; God be with you till we meet a-gain.

**CHORUS**

Till we meet,.... till we meet, Till we meet at Je-sus' feet;
Till we meet, till we meet, till we meet;

Till we meet,.... till we meet, God be with you till we meet a-gain.
Till we meet, till we meet,

# Topical Index

## CHILDREN

| | |
|---|---|
| As a Volunteer | 24 |
| Bring Them In | 132 |
| Dare to Be a Daniel | 96 |
| Do You Wonder Why? | 99 |
| Everybody Ought to Love Jesus | 98 |
| God Has Blotted Them Out | 97 |
| He Keeps Me Singing | 5 |
| I Am So Glad That Jesus Loves Me | 92 |
| Into My Heart | 95 |
| Jesus Loves Even Me | 92 |
| No Longer Lonely | 84 |
| Onward, Christian Soldiers | 114 |
| Shine Just Where You Are | 100 |
| Tell Me the Stories of Jesus | 101 |
| Win Them One by One | 16 |
| Wonderful Things to Know | 94 |

## CHOIR

| | |
|---|---|
| All Hail, Immanuel | 109 |
| Awakening Chorus | 105 |
| Beloved, Now Are We | 110 |
| Hallelujah for the Cross! | 104 |
| Seeking the Lost | 121 |
| The Song of the Soldier | 106 |
| Thy Kingdom Come | 107 |
| Wonderful Grace of Jesus | 108 |

## CHORUSES

| | |
|---|---|
| Do You Wonder Why? | 99 |
| Everybody Ought to Love Jesus | 98 |
| God Has Blotted Them Out | 97 |
| Into My Heart | 95 |
| Shine Just Where You Are | 100 |

## CONSECRATION

| | |
|---|---|
| Close to Thee | 146 |
| Fill Me Now | 148 |
| Have Thine Own Way, Lord | 1 |
| I Am Coming, Lord | 131 |
| I Am Thine, O Lord | 73 |
| I'll Live for Him | 111 |
| Jesus Calls Us | 161 |
| Speak, My Lord | 30 |
| Take Time to Be Holy | 41 |
| Where He Leads Me | 128 |

## CROSS

| | |
|---|---|
| Alas! and Did My Saviour Bleed? | 135 |
| At Calvary | 79 |
| Glory to His Name | 133 |
| I Am Coming to the Cross | 43 |
| In the Cross of Christ | 138 |
| Jesus Paid It All | 127 |
| Must Jesus Bear the Cross Alone? | 170 |
| Near the Cross | 136 |
| Nothing But the Blood | 29 |
| Saved by the Blood | 33 |
| The Old Rugged Cross | 2 |
| The Way of the Cross Leads Home | 13 |
| There Is a Fountain | 145 |
| There Is Power in the Blood | 31 |
| When I Survey the Wondrous Cross | 165 |

## DEVOTIONAL

| | |
|---|---|
| A Charge to Keep | 141 |
| Alas! and Did My Saviour Bleed? | 135 |
| All Hail the Power | 112 |
| Amazing Grace | 156 |

## DEVOTIONAL—Continued

| | |
|---|---|
| Blessed Assurance | 68 |
| Blest Be the Tie | 169 |
| Break Thou the Bread of Life | 162 |
| Come, Thou Almighty King | 134 |
| Come, Thou Fount | 103 |
| Faith of Our Fathers | 159 |
| Hallelujah, What a Saviour | 142 |
| Holy Spirit, Faithful Guide | 139 |
| How Firm a Foundation | 152 |
| I Love Thy Kingdom, Lord | 158 |
| In the Cross of Christ | 138 |
| Jesus, Lover of My Soul | 168 |
| Jesus Shall Reign | 163 |
| Must Jesus Bear the Cross Alone? | 170 |
| My Faith Looks Up to Thee | 151 |
| My Jesus, I Love Thee | 140 |
| Nearer, My God, to Thee | 167 |
| O Happy Day | 149 |
| O Worship the King | 59 |
| O Zion, Haste | 164 |
| Pass Me Not | 67 |
| Rock of Ages | 166 |
| Sweet Hour of Prayer | 55 |
| Take Time to Be Holy | 41 |
| The Solid Rock | 69 |
| What a Friend | 144 |
| When I Survey the Wondrous Cross | 165 |

## INVITATION

| | |
|---|---|
| Almost Persuaded | 126 |
| Bring Them In | 132 |
| I Am Coming, Lord | 131 |
| I Am Coming to the Cross | 43 |
| I Am Praying for You | 72 |
| Into My Heart | 95 |
| Jesus, I Come | 122 |
| Jesus Is Calling | 118 |
| Jesus Paid It All | 127 |
| Just as I Am | 130 |
| Let Jesus Come Into Your Heart | 120 |
| Lord, I'm Coming Home | 129 |
| Only Trust Him | 150 |
| Seeking the Lost | 121 |
| Softly and Tenderly | 119 |
| There Is Power in the Blood | 31 |
| While Jesus Whispers to You | 125 |
| Why Not Now? | 123 |

## MISSIONARY

| | |
|---|---|
| Here Am I, Send Me | 124 |
| Jesus Is Calling | 118 |
| The Call for Reapers | 147 |
| Throw Out the Life-Line | 65 |
| We've a Story to Tell | 77 |
| Where He Leads Me | 128 |

## SERVICE

| | |
|---|---|
| As a Volunteer | 24 |
| Bring Them In | 132 |
| Here Am I, Send Me | 124 |
| I Love to Tell the Story | 81 |
| Just a Little Help from You | 37 |
| Rescue the Perishing | 64 |
| The Call for Reapers | 147 |
| Where He Leads Me | 128 |
| Win Them One by One | 16 |
| Work, for the Night Is Coming | 157 |

# Index

## A

| | |
|---|---|
| A Charge to Keep | 141 |
| A Great Salvation | 45 |
| Alas! and Did My Saviour Bleed? | 135 |
| All Hail, Immanuel | 109 |
| All Hail the Power | 112 |
| All Hail the Power (Miles Lane) | 113 |
| Almost Persuaded | 126 |
| Amazing Grace | 156 |
| America | 116 |
| America, the Beautiful | 117 |
| As a Volunteer | 24 |
| At Calvary | 79 |
| Awakening Chorus | 105 |

## B

| | |
|---|---|
| Be Like Jesus | 38 |
| Beloved, Now Are We | 110 |
| Beulah Land | 75 |
| Beulah Land, Dwelling in | 28 |
| Blessed Assurance | 68 |
| Blest Be the Tie | 169 |
| Break Thou the Bread of Life | 162 |
| Bring Them In | 132 |

## C

| | |
|---|---|
| Call for Reapers, The | 147 |
| Charge to Keep, A | 141 |
| Christ Arose | 7 |
| Christ Liveth in Me | 71 |
| Christ Receiveth Sinful Men | 50 |
| Christ Returneth | 51 |
| Close to Thee | 146 |
| Come, Thou Almighty King | 134 |
| Come, Thou Fount | 103 |
| Coming Home, Coming Home | 129 |

## D

| | |
|---|---|
| Dare to Be a Daniel | 96 |
| Do You Wonder Why? | 99 |
| Down at the Cross | 133 |
| Draw Me Nearer | 73 |
| Dwelling in Beulah Land | 28 |

## E

| | |
|---|---|
| Everybody Ought to Love Jesus | 98 |

## F

| | |
|---|---|
| Faith Is the Victory | 78 |
| Faith of Our Fathers | 159 |
| Fight Is On, The | 66 |
| Fill Me Now | 148 |
| For You I Am Praying | 72 |

## G

| | |
|---|---|
| Glory Song, The | 91 |
| Glory to His Name | 133 |
| God Be with You | 171 |
| God Has Blotted Them Out | 97 |
| Great Salvation, A | 45 |

## H

| | |
|---|---|
| Hallelujah for the Cross! | 104 |
| Hallelujah, What a Saviour | 142 |
| Happy Day, O | 149 |
| Have Thine Own Way, Lord | 1 |
| He Hideth My Soul | 83 |
| He Included Me | 21 |
| He Keeps Me Singing | 5 |
| He Lifted Me | 93 |
| He Lives on High | 27 |
| He Ransomed Me | 34 |
| He Will Hold Me Fast | 56 |
| He's a Wonderful Saviour to Me | 12 |
| Here Am I, Send Me | 124 |
| Higher Ground | 82 |
| Holy Spirit, Faithful Guide | 139 |
| How Firm a Foundation (Portugese) | 152 |
| How Firm a Foundation | 153 |

## I

| | |
|---|---|
| I Am Coming, Lord | 131 |
| I Am Coming to the Cross | 43 |
| I Am Praying for You | 72 |
| I Am So Glad That Jesus Loves Me | 92 |
| I Am Thine, O Lord | 73 |
| I Choose Jesus | 63 |
| I Know Whom I Have Believed | 32 |
| I Love to Tell the Story | 81 |
| I Love Thy Kingdom, Lord | 158 |
| I Need Jesus | 19 |
| I Need Thee Every Hour | 23 |
| I Stand Amazed in the Presence | 39 |
| I Walk with the King | 11 |
| I Will Sing of My Redeemer | 48 |
| I Will Sing the Wondrous Story | 4 |
| I Would Be Like Jesus | 38 |
| I'll Live for Him | 111 |
| If Jesus Goes with Me | 22 |
| In Loving Kindness Jesus Came | 93 |
| In My Heart There Rings a Melody | 9 |
| In the Cross of Christ | 138 |
| In the Garden | 6 |
| In the Sweet By and By | 62 |
| Into My Heart | 95 |
| Is It the Crowning Day? | 20 |
| Is My Name Written There? | 90 |
| It Is Glory Just to Walk with Him | 76 |
| Ivory Palaces | 60 |

## J

| | |
|---|---|
| Jesus Calls Us | 161 |
| Jesus, I Come | 122 |
| Jesus Is Calling | 118 |
| Jesus, Jesus, Jesus | 5 |
| Jesus, Keep Me Near the Cross | 136 |
| Jesus, Lover of My Soul | 168 |
| Jesus Loves Even Me | 92 |
| Jesus Paid It All | 127 |
| Jesus Saves | 70 |
| Jesus Shall Reign | 163 |
| Just a Little Help from You | 37 |
| Just as I Am | 130 |
| Just Now, Your Doubtings | 129 |

## L

| | |
|---|---|
| Leaning on the Everlasting Arms | 35 |
| Let Jesus Come into Your Heart | 120 |
| Let the Lower Lights Be Burning | 102 |
| Lord, I'm Coming Home | 129 |
| Love Found a Way | 36 |
| Love Lifted Me | 3 |

## M

| | |
|---|---|
| Man of Sorrows | 142 |
| Must Jesus Bear the Cross Alone? | 170 |

My Anchor Holds.................. 54
My Country, 'Tis of Thee...........116
My Faith Looks Up to Thee........151
My Hope Is Built on Nothing Less.. 69
My Jesus, I Love Thee.............140
My Redeemer...................... 48
My Saviour's Love................. 39

### N

Near the Cross....................136
Nearer, My God, to Thee...........167
Ninety and Nine, The.............. 18
No Longer Lonely.................. 84
Nothing But the Blood............. 29

### O

O Happy Day......................149
O That Will Be Glory............. 91
O Worship the King................ 59
O Zion, Haste....................164
Oh, How I Love Jesus.............154
Old Rugged Cross, The.............  2
On Jordan's Stormy Banks.........155
On the Homeward Way............. 53
One Day!......................... 40
Only a Sinner.................... 87
Only Trust Him...................150
Onward, Christian Soldiers........114

### P

Pass Me Not...................... 67

### R

Rescue the Perishing.............. 64
Revive Us Again..................143
Rock of Ages.....................166

### S

Sail On!......................... 17
Saved!........................... 46
Saved by Grace................... 61
Saved by the Blood............... 33
Saved, Saved!.................... 10
Seeking the Lost.................121
Shine Just Where You Are.........100
Showers of Blessing.............. 52
Since I Have Been Redeemed....... 25
Since Jesus Came into My Heart....  8
Since the Fullness of His Love Came In 88
Softly and Tenderly..............119
Solid Rock, The.................. 69
Song of the Soldier, The.........106
Speak, My Lord................... 30
Stand Up For Jesus...............137
Sweet By and By.................. 62
Sweet Hour of Prayer............. 55
Sweeter as the Years Go By....... 14

### T

Take the Name of Jesus with You... 49
Take Time to Be Holy............. 41
Tell Me the Stories of Jesus........101
The Call for Reapers..............147
The Fight Is On.................. 66
The Glory Song................... 91
The Ninety and Nine.............. 18
The Old Rugged Cross.............  2
The Solid Rock................... 69
The Song of the Soldier..........106
The Victory Side................. 15
The Way of the Cross Leads Home.. 13
There Is a Fountain..............145
There Is a Name I Love to Hear....154
There Is Power in the Blood........ 31
There Shall Be Showers of Blessing. 52
There Were Ninety and Nine....... 18
There's a Great Day Coming........115
There's Within My Heart a Melody..  5
Throw Out the Life-Line.......... 65
Thy Kingdom Come.................107
'Tis So Sweet to Trust in Jesus..... 89
Trust and Obey................... 86

### U

Under His Wings.................. 57

### V

Victory Side, The................ 15

### W

Way of the Cross, The............ 13
We Praise Thee, O God!...........143
We're Marching to Zion........... 74
We've a Story to Tell............ 77
What a Fellowship................ 35
What a Friend....................144
What Can Wash Away My Sin?.... 29
What If It Were Today?........... 42
When I Survey the Wondrous Cross.165
When the Roll Is Called Up Yonder. 58
When They Ring the Golden Bells... 44
When We All Get to Heaven....... 47
Where He Leads Me...............128
Where the Gates Swing Outward Never 26
While Jesus Whispers to You......125
Whosoever, Meaneth Me............ 85
Why Not Now?....................123
Win Them One by One............. 16
Wonderful Grace of Jesus..........108
Wonderful Things to Know......... 94
Wonderful Words of Life..........160
Work, For the Night Is Coming.....157
Would You Be Free................ 31

### Y

Ye Must Be Born Again............ 80